THE RIDDLE
OF THE FLYING SAUCERS

Is Another World Watching?

THE RIDDLE
OF THE FLYING SAUCERS

Is Another World Watching?

by

GERALD HEARD

LONDON
CARROLL & NICHOLSON

First Published 1950

Printed by Winter & Worsfold, Ltd.,
14 Verney Road, London

MADE IN GREAT BRITAIN

FOREWORD

THIS report covers just over three years—from Midsummer 1947 to late Summer and early Autumn 1950. It is an attempt to give in some chronological order the development of a series of phenomena which is quite unprecedented—at least in persistence, in extent, in the numbers of objects seen and the numbers of witnesses involved.

It is clear now, beyond any possibility of reasonable doubt, that not only has something been continually haunting the upper skies of the vast area of land comprised between the Western Provinces of Canada and the Northern States of Mexico; but also, further than that, the phenomena, though varied in some particulars, do all of them fall into certain categories. What has been seen over these years, and is still being seen to the last moment of reporting, is some sort of super flying-machine (the old fashioned name is used because some of the craft are clearly not 'planes' in any exact sense of the word. Also, it is possible that some do not 'plane' at all—that is, keep themselves up in the air by the pressure of the air on a flat underside—some seem to be able to roll along as comfortably as cart-wheels on their rims).

The problem then arises, and it is an acute one, second to none in immediate importance to all the peoples of this world: who controls these machines, who has made them, whence do they come? This report therefore goes on, using all the material we have of skilled observation and deduction, to try to define this problem. Considering the craft and their performance, what can we learn about them, their possible crews, their possible home base? Considering the way they have behaved toward us, can we make any suppositions as to the kind of mind that is behind these quick-flashing, enigmatic masks? Step by step the argument and evidence lead us on.

Of course any conclusions, on such evidence as we have, can only be deductive, circumstantial. But there seems too much evidence to say merely "There is no possible theory of any sort to cover these oddities, the freaks of the upper sky, these complete anomalies". In a case like this everyone must draw his own conclusions. But he must be given all the evidence—even the oddest—if it is well vouched for—i.e. made by several skilled witnesses able to form judgments of value and under favourable conditions of observation. And the reader must also be given such reasons as point to any valid conclusions—conclusions that are not contrary to logic. That is what this report has attempted to furnish.

G. H.

CONTENTS

Foreword

LIST OF ILLUSTRATIONS

Chapter I

HOW THE SAGA STARTED

TUESDAY 24th June 1947 may prove to be one of the most important dates in History. It is the birthday of the oddest and indeed the biggest story that ever troubled news-editors. And troubled is the right word. For most big stories are editors' delight. But this — this has proved a headache. For the fact is, it has been just a bit too big. It is true enough, if human evidence, masses of it given by competent observers, is to be trusted.

But then again, it just cannot be! Why? Because if it is true it is incredible!

But surely some sensible explanation can be found? That is the second and equally odd part of the story. As the evidence was good, editors and all sensible readers tried to squeeze the facts into a common-sense explanation.

But it was no use. Like the Genie, once it got out of the bottle, this huge story would not fit into any sensible theory. Editor after editor, science editors, aviation editors, editors-in-chief all worked on the brute fact. They tried to get at high-up people — Air Force authorities, presidents of aircraft companies, staff officers, the President of the United States.

Would no one take this monster under his wing and say reassuringly, "It is really a new invention made by us, it is a secret weapon, it is an original space-ship."? But none of them would. Why? Well, again no one is sure and your guess is as good as the next man's, provided you read all the accounts which so far have been published by reputable news agencies.

So here is the story, here are the series of incidents, happenings, phenomena that have caused more trouble in the news than any historical mystery up to date.

On that Tuesday 24th June 1947, Kenneth Arnold, aged 32,

well-educated, a fine athlete, a successful businessman was flying his own plane. He is an aviator of experience. He has a business of his own, called the Great Western Fire Control Supply Company, and he handles, distributes and installs fire-fighting equipment through the Northwestern States of America. He is a good pilot, too. He visits his clients all over his big business territory, landing in meadows, etc. He lives at Boise, Idaho. He was returning there from the town of Chehalis, in Washington State. His next stop was to be at Yakima, also in Washington, but he made a detour. For flyers had been asked to keep a look-out when flying in that district. A large air-transport carrying troops was believed to have crashed near the south-west side of the snow mountain that stands up from the great Rockies range where it runs north and south through Washington State.

Mount Rainier was a dazzling sight that day. Arnold rose to nearly 10,000 feet and skirted the huge platform from which the peak itself rises. So he was able to scan the desolate giant gullies in any one of which he might see the wreckage of the lost plane. The weather was so good that he could give all his attention to the view.

Then a flash caught Arnold's eye. He turned and looked in that direction. Nine objects were flying like a line of geese, and they were swerving in perfect formation in and out of the mountain peaks. Arnold thought they must be some twenty miles or more from him. For two minutes he watched them in their swift, closely co-ordinated flight, timing himself by his cockpit clock. He also estimated their speed by the rate at which they passed the land-marks—the snow peaks he knew. The pace was somewhere about 1000 miles per hour. The speed was of course high, very high, too high for 1947. The course the covey took over the peaks was not sane human flying. But it was the shape of the objects that stumped the observer. They were unlike any plane that he knew. They were discs, they were saucers.

Arnold talked about what he had seen as soon as he was down. Flying men, having satisfied themselves that he had not been taken in by some mirage effect, told him he must have seen jet-planes, or some secret weapon of the Government — or of another Government.

Then the news spread and the story began to find echoes. Till almost the beginning of July the papers were open to such reports. Then suddenly they were seized with shyness. 'Mass hallucination' became the pass-word. Such a widely informed and open-minded authority as Waldemar Kaempffert, veteran Science Editor of *The New York Times*, gave that as his opinion. But the reports didn't stop, though now they had to be hunted out from small daily paper files, whose correspondents found that local interest counted for more than nation-wide ridicule. A United Press correspondent in Arnold's home town of Boise, believed he saw discs in the sky. So did Johnson, news editor of *The Daily Statesman* of the town. A United Air Lines plane going out of Boise also, before July was over, reported that the saucers had been seen.

Boise was evidently a good centre for observation. But though the Northwest seemed at first to be the favourite patrolling ground for these ceiling-cruisers, they were soon heard of from all over the West. *The Arizona Republic*, a paper published in the big resort town of Phoenix, printed two photographs taken by a Mr. Rhodes of that city. They show, in the larger photograph, a thing more like a black rubber heel with a small hole in the middle of it than a saucer. But it is certainly some sort of flying-plane with the back of the heel acting as the prow. That was on the 9th July; but this story, with its photographs and with the evidence of a number of witnesses who said that the photographs were of the object they had seen at that time, awoke no echoes in the rest of the Press. The second of the very odd features of this oddest of stories had come, like the ghost of Hamlet's father on to the stage.

To the fact that something extremely strange had been seen, had certainly been seen, was now added the remarkable behaviour of the information-givers, the Press and the Air-authorities. From here on, two factors are in play together through this baffling story. Something of the highest interest, the most pressing concern has been seen, seen again and again, continues to be seen, and by most competent observers: *and* something which cannot be seen, cannot be tracked, persists in keeping the subject out of the big papers, making out that people who see such things must be subject to 'hallucinations'.

The whole thing is uncannily like that other eerie subject, Psychical Research. There, too, we find the same baffling pattern. Researchers or observers say they have seen something very odd— they are convinced that they viewed some strange, inexplicable phenomena. All the authorities say "Nonsense" and add, "No trained observer ever sees such things". Then a trained observer does see and tell. For example, ranking scientists such as Crookes, Lodge, Flammarion, great thinkers like Henri Bergson and William James, say they have investigated and found evidence. What happens? The vast mass of laboratory workers all reply, "Poor old men, going off their heads!" When Freud asserted that he had found evidence of Extra-sensory Perception, the same thing was said of him by some of his own lieutenants, "more royalist than the king".

The same thing happened with meteorites. Learned societies in the nineteenth century agreed that papers reporting such things must not be published. For the sky is not a blue vault off which pieces of the plaster flake and fall to the ground. Therefore meteorites are not possible. "Why?" asked Lavoisier, the great French savant, with the assured satire of the uninformed expert who knows all the answers to the questions he asks, "Why do intelligent, scientific persons never see meteorites?" And he answers, "Because of course a trained mind would immediately perceive that what was thought to be a meteor was only the vulgar misapprehension of an uneducated person".

A perfect example of this sort of thing is actually supplied in this Disc Dilemma by the example cited above—the case of the United Air Lines plane that was flying from Boise on the afternoon of 4th July 1947. The day is of course a great one for Americans. So when at Portland, Oregon, and Seattle, Washington, numbers of people saw discs flashing about high up in the sky — competent estimation gave the height as 10,000 feet—there was a fine mixture of comment—"The Government choosing the right day to show us we are all right"—"Some other Government looking in to see if any of the home team would like to do a bit of stratosphere racing?"—"Some sort of upper atmosphere oddity of firework display". (The day is a great one for pyrotechnics).

Experts, who did not get a look, naturally said there was really nothing to see. One of them was the Captain of the United Air Lines 'ship' leaving Boise. He did not have to wait long. Close to sunset right ahead of the plane obligingly appeared five 'saucers'. The Captain and his First Officer rang for the plane's 'Hostess'. The three watched the five objects and when these had allowed themselves to be observed for some minutes, four more joined the original five. This space-circus performed in front of the three observers for the best part of ten minutes and then disappeared. How far away the objects were, and what their size, none of the three could of course be sure.

The three reported what they had seen. But they got no help. The Air Force and the Navy both said they had nothing of that sort on the earth, still less in the sky.

Chapter II

THE MYSTERY OF MAURY ISLAND

MEANWHILE, to muddle things still further, came what we may call the Maury Island Mystery. Arnold, we see, had talked of his experience; and the idea that discs were about was certainly 'in the air'. Arnold was asked by a luncheon club to which he belonged in his home town of Boise to address them on the queer topic. He mentioned a rumour that had come to him that the Harbour Patrol Staff at the Washington port of Tacoma had not only 'seen things'. They had fragments of something dropped from the sky.

After Arnold's address a fellow member said that he had worked on that Harbour Patrol and knew one of its staff named Dahl, a reliable fellow. Johnson, aviation editor of the Boise paper, who himself had sighted what he believed to be a disc, told Arnold that he thought he ought to follow up this clue. Arnold agreed and started out early on the 30th July. A couple of hours later he was rewarded by sighting a flight of saucers. He snapshotted at them but got no convincing film record—only a few dots.

Arriving at a Tacoma hotel, Arnold rang up Dahl. But Dahl did not want to talk—in fact actually said the subject had better be left alone. (This, it should be noted, does not seem the mark of someone anxious to get into the news). However, at last Dahl came along and gave his tale.

Maury Island is a small uninhabited place three miles out from Tacoma port. The harbour patrol-boat was close to the island's shore. Dahl said he had a crew of two men and his son with him. It was close on 2 p.m. on the 21st June — the longest day of the year. Dahl, at the wheel, suddenly noticed (this suddenness of the appearances is one of the odd but consistent features of these visits) half a dozen large discs directly above the boat and apparently only 2000 feet up in the air. They at first seemed to be hanging motionless. Then five could be seen to be moving slowly

16

round one in the centre. That was moving too. But it was settling down, sinking towards the sea till it was judged to be no more than 500 feet above the water. There, however, it paused. The monsters made not a whisper, seemed to be about 100 feet across, and each had a large hollow axis. They shone in the sun.

The crew—perhaps not unnaturally—were frightened and turned the boat to the beach. But once there they took several photographs. Next there came in the silence a boom: and the disc nearest the water suddenly let fall first a light-coloured and then a dark metal object. Some of the fragments on touching the water raised steam—evidently they were intensely hot. The disc, so lightened, rose again, and the whole six went off to sea. (This exit over the Pacific seems, incidentally, a favourite closing line of the performances of such discs on the West Coast. This raises the question whether those who control them have no fear of the sea and regard it rather as a safe hide-out from human attention).

An oil-tanker, the S.S. Ticonderoga, for instance, on 12th November 1947 reported, when 25 miles off the Oregon coast, that two discs were sighted rushing out to sea, headed south-west, a direction that leads to the greatest space of water on the surface of the globe.

Dahl, as was his duty, on his return to harbour told his superior officer, Crisman, what he had seen. He gave Crisman the camera with which the photographs had been taken and fragments of the strange metal which Dahl claimed had fallen from the sky. To this account he added a further oddity, more of the category of the detective story than of the science-invention scripts and forecasts. He said that he had received warnings not to speak of what he had seen—warnings given by a quite ordinary looking man. Nevertheless he was willing to show Arnold the metal. Arnold was disappointed. He thought that the mineral was only lava rock.

Crisman was questioned. He said that on the 23rd June he followed up the Dahl story, taking the harbour patrol boat out to Maury Island, where he found tons of slag there. Further, he added, while he was inspecting he found he was being inspected. Out of the sky came a disc, made a turn of the bay and then dived into a cumulus thunder-cloud—an odd hang-up for any flyer. Crisman also promised to show Arnold the photographs, and to

17

conduct him to the island. Arnold was impressed—coast-guards are responsible persons and trained in careful observation. Indeed, in spite of the slag not being what he hoped, he felt that what he had heard was so important that he thought that he ought to have a second witness with him. And who could be better than Captain E. J. Smith, the skipper of the air-liner which, sailing from Boise over Idaho State on that 4th July, had, with his co-pilot and the liner's Hostess, seen nine discs dancing ahead of the plane?

Before Arnold summoned Smith he called Military Intelligence and asked for Lieutenant Brown. Brown was down at Hamilton Field, a big air centre near San Francisco. Arnold asked Brown to come up, and then fetched Smith from Seattle to Tacoma. Crisman met Smith and took him out. Therefore Arnold was alone when late in the afternoon of the 31st July Lieutenant Brown and a Captain Davidson turned up, having flown up from Hamilton Field in a B.25 Bomber. Crisman and Smith returned, and Crisman repeated his story. Dahl was not present. The slag fragments were shown again. Brown and Davidson did not seem impressed and after some further conversations said they must fly back. They took, however, a fair-sized cardboard box of the stuff with them. They said they would be unable to visit the island.

Arnold and Smith stayed the night at Tacoma. When they woke up in their hotel, they were told that Crisman was on the telephone. He told them that the plane in which Brown and Davidson had flown back had crashed, and that both had been killed.

The crashing of the plane had a number of odd features about it. Why did two other occupants, enlisted men, get safely out in parachutes eleven minutes before the plane itself crashed; and why, considering the time between the engine catching fire and the plane crashing, was the plane, itself not on fire and not slowed down to minimise the crash?

Arnold and Smith made a date with Crisman to visit Maury Island and examine the slag. When they reached the patrol-boat the engine was found 'dead'. Further, though Dahl had said that the boat had been hit by the falling slag from the disc, the damage did not appear to Arnold and Smith to be as serious as they felt he had made out. Crisman insisted that there was nothing to do but wait till the engine was repaired: he would call them when it was ready. He never did. Nor could he be found. Arnold called Dahl, who said Crisman had left town on business. But a newspaper man known to Arnold said that Crisman had gone on an Army plane bound for Alaska. The efforts to get the photographs proved futile: the film had been taken out of town. Smith got in touch with a Major Sanders of Air Intelligence, who heard Arnold's story. "The metal's just slag", he said "and the story is a hoax."

For some time, this was the Defence Forces' official answer to all reports. But the explanation did not cover all the facts. For instance, before Brown and Davidson had left on their fatal flight, they had in his hotel room described to Arnold what discs were like.

So the Disc Drama opened. Its first scene epitomised the whole play down to date. Throughout we find the same trio of factors present:—

(i) The honest, competent observer, who sees clearly something he cannot explain and never expected;

(ii) The narrator who quite possibly has seen something very odd, but who has some reason or reasons for never saying clearly and unequivocally what it is, and who after several hesitations shuts down and fades out; and

(iii) The Professional Authorities and the Defence Forces. These are never free to disclose all they know, still less what they may suspect. Therefore, they can feel nothing but relief when they can honestly conclude and give as their opinion on the whole, in view of the existence of doubtful reporting, exaggeration and tale-spinning, "It's all mal-observation. It's all a mistake".

But the United States is a free country. You may (except in war-time) ask any question you like of anyone, right up to the President; and get an answer, indeed many answers, if you are the Press. The Press might not want to print all it was told. But it was clear that the various official sources of air-information must have been interested in the question whether they alone had the sky as their patrolling ground. As early as 8th July 1947 Muroc Flying Field Staff saw half a dozen saucers. This was group observation by trained observers. Hallucination is spun of thinner stuff.

Saucer reports could now be listed from forty of the forty-eight States—so the country had been well covered by the sky-saunterers. In Idaho was reported a disc which had swooped so low at Twin Falls that the tree tops bowed to it. The Cascade Mountains in Oregon brought a companion piece. There Fred Johnson, a prospector for ores, saw five or six discs flashing in the sun. He was able to range his telescope on them while they played aloft for fifty seconds.

This was the day—24th June 1947—that Arnold made his first statement; but Fred Johnson was not then aware of it. What made his glimpses of the discs memorable was that the needle of the compass he was wearing was violently agitated. This may seem unimportant: but hints are presented throughout the entire story that the discs may derive their power from a form of energy of which today we have only the faintest speculative notion. In other words, they may be actuated by some type of magnetic power which enables them to resist the pull of gravity.

At this point may be summarised such evidence as seems to have been presented to the judgment senses of so many and such widely scattered Americans.

To the fact that discs had frequently been seen flashing in the sun was now to be added their presence at night. The oddest thing about them so far was not their shape nor their speed. There *could* in the future be a disc plane—a giant quoit is a shape* for which plane-designers believe there is something to be said. The speed of these objects seemed to be about 1000 miles per hour—exceeding the speed of sound which so many theorists, said we should never pass. Yet it leaked out that human airmen had in the autumn of the "DISC YEAR"—1947—exceeded that speed (700 miles an hour). The real surprise was not something

---

* This shape has often been the subject of speculation, but it presents at present very serious obstacles to designers so long as we have only the existing means of powering a plane. An independent inventor named Jonthan Caldwell, who worked by himself on this problem on a farm in Pennsylvania, did leave a large model of such a craft. Then he disappeared, and has not been traced. When the decayed model was found, some investigators thought it might be the first sketch for the present discs. It is clear, however, that the investigator never brought his craft beyond the model stage, and had not solved any of the real problems of Disc flight.

that the discs had, but something they did not have—the man-made plane's most tell-tale feature, its torrent of 'give-away' sound.

The discs were dumb.

True, the photographer who saw, at Phoenix, Arizona, a disc making a turn that would plunge a pilot into a "black-out", reported that he did hear a "swoosh". But otherwise the objects swept through the atmosphere as silently as if it were a searchlight beam, darting through a cloud.

A further example of this was afforded by a big flight—viewed in the stillness of the late evening in the Southern State of Louisiana. In perfect silence and yet at headlong speed across the sky ran scores of objects—and they were luminous. Nearly all observers agreed that, in the sunlight, they gleamed like metal. But dusk disclosed this other strange feature—the glow probably as significant as, and perhaps linked up with—their silence.

We may of course say of the observation made in Louisiana, and of this whole group of sightings, of which there are many, "But surely they *are* only a series of searchlight beams running through the upper air and glowing on faint streaks of cloud, otherwise invisible!"

Chapter III

WHAT TWO PASSENGER-PLANE PILOTS SAW

AT this point we come upon an important new fact. We now meet not only fresh evidence—unknown air-ships, yes, a completely different pattern even from that of the discs—another 'genus'—rushing headlong through the night and showing lights as strange as their shape—but another fact to match it, a fact as firm as the first fact is unsettling.

Up till now we have had to depend on only two types of evidence:

(i) That of people on the earth suddenly caught by surprise, not on the look-out, straining up to the sky and seeing for a few moments, at uncertain heights, objects flashing and dancing — almost the worst type of observation even when the observers are trained to look for sky travellers. It is amazing that any photographs have been secured. No wonder they tell us little.

(ii) The second type of evidence is more reliable: that from men actually up in planes.

Even here, as with the observations of Arnold and Smith, the lookers-on had to own they could not judge the distance or be very sure of the shape of the discs which Arnold thought were twenty miles away. A ship twenty miles off need not fear much from inspection by the naked eye.

What was most needed at this point was observation made by a couple of trained flyers, trained of course to recognise aircraft, up in the air and (as even Smith was not) abreast of their quarry, on the same level as the object which they observed; and, if at all possible, really close to it.

All this was now to be granted. Captain C. S. Chiles, accompanied by his First Officer, J. B. Whitted, was flying a passenger plane from Houston, Texas, on a standard flight to Atlanta, Georgia, and thence to Boston, Massachusetts. The two officers were on the staff of Eastern Airlines Incorporated. Both had fine records in the war, and equally good ones as careful and highly responsible pilots while they had been in civilian air-service.

The plane left at 8.30 p.m. on 23rd July 1948. At 2.45 a.m. there was a good moon coming through broken cloud.

Suddenly a brilliant super-giant torpedo dashed towards the Eastern Airlines ship. Both flying officers saw it. It was coming straight down the air-traffic lane they were on. But it was a little above them. Then it suddenly swooped down. Captain Chiles swung his plane violently to the left. Fortunately the monster veered as sharply to the right, and they rushed past each other.

The pilots stared as the object flew past only some 700 feet away. It was close enough for them to see that it had no wings! About 100 feet long, this cigar-shaped body was sinister enough. But its lighting seemed even more baleful. It had a fore-cabin or look-out port. So it was evidently a 'manned' or inhabited object—or, to be still more cautious, let us say it seemed to need to see. But the light that came from the cabin surely would make anyone inside incapable of seeing anything outside even in daylight, let alone at night. For this fore-part glared as though someone were burning magnesium flares inside.

Nor was that all. Right along the side of this fish-like monster that swam the air, throughout its length as down the sides of some of those deep-sea monsters that dwell in total dark, ran a vivid purplish band of glowing light.

To complete its weird lighting, there spouted from the back of the hull an orange flame which, as it fanned out, spreading in a tail, turned into a delicate yellow. This great fan of flame was half as long again as the hundred-foot craft that spouted it. A life-like, if not a human, touch was given by two rows of windows. But in the moment that they flashed by, the two astounded pilots did not see any watching faces pressed against the panes.

But some guiding intelligence, not unaware of peril and desirous of avoiding disaster, was in control of this great shaft of speeding force. And 'he' was as skilful as he was—if a little late in the day —considerate. His method of showing this was none the less alarming. This flukeless black whale of the upper air suddenly doubled its awe-inspiring fan-tail of flame. This gave the whole

23

craft a kick as if it had been shot from a gun and the entire ship soared like an arrow and plunged into the clouds above.

The pilots had not merely to trust their eyes for this manoeuvre. As their momentary and profoundly disturbing companion took leave, its leap into the upper sky caused such a 'wash' in the air that the passenger plane gave a confirmatory and very unsettling lurch. Captain Chiles at once went into the passenger section of the ship, leaving his second officer to fly the craft. He must find out if anyone else saw what he and Whitted had seen. It was the dead-hour of the night—2.45 a.m. But one passenger, a Mr. McKelvie, did see the light rush past close to them. And he did note that it was a light unlike any light he had ever seen—neither lightning nor the friendly lights of earth.

Tracking the story—which had a big press for the moment—it was found that about 2 a.m. that night, air observers at the flying field of the city of Macon in Georgia had seen rushing overhead a long, dark wingless tube that evidently hurled itself along by means of the huge flame that spurted from the stern. The Navy authorities suggested, as their reply to the question, "What in heaven's name was that?", that it might be one of the super-rockets which everyone knew were being experimented with in New Mexico. (These will have a later chapter to themselves). But could a stray rocket wander alone over so much of the United States? Surely, even an adequately self-guided missile could hardly prove as willing and able to yield right of way, as this super-giant torpedo had done? What we can ask, with more chance of getting an answer, is—had any report of any sort come to hand of this 'new' type of unknown flyer—a non-disc?

The answer to that, is Yes. A big wingless shaft of a thing like a log in a stream, plunged across the traffic lane being followed at Bethel, Alabama by two airmen working for a local flying service. But this seemed to have no glow and not even a wake. The two airmen tried to follow but it outpaced them—they were trotting along at under 200 miles per hour. That was in August 1947, at the beginning of the excitement.

And to start 1948 well, on the 1st January a 'ship' of the same non-committal cut showed up over the Southern State of

Mississippi. Again a couple of flyers saw it from their plane and tried to follow. Again, just by doubling its pace, almost at a bound, as usual it shot ahead. But this time people on the ground saw it as well.

Fortunately at this point, too, we get something like what opticians call 'binocular vision'—that is to say we get a report from far outside the United States and from one of the most down-to-earth and wordly-wise communities on this earth—from Holland. In July 1948, a few days before Chiles and Whitted had their experience, a wingless sky-charger, straight as a pole, but showing lines of windows or ports, had rushed across the Netherlands, very fast, very high, said the astounded Dutchmen.

Now in all this confusion of really too much evidence—so confusing because of its richness—we can begin to sort out the findings.

First and foremost we can be sure that while there may be many different kinds of discs—different species, as biologists would say, different species of one genus,—the saucer—there are also riding the upper air, and perhaps riding above and beyond the upper air, another 'genus'—this long straight tube.

That raises a further question—Can we stop at two? If two, why not three and more? As H. G. Wells used to remark when people tried to use the 'shut-down' of the 'either-or' argument— "The Mind of the Universe can count above two". That further question has an answer in the affirmative—but, alas, that does not mean that this answer has proved reassuring to anyone—quite the reverse! And with that question (for as a matter of fact both are linked) we may raise the other question which we have all been asking "Surely someone could grapple with this kind of trespasser? We no longer have to stand on the ground, rooted by gravity and gaze helplessly at the sky. We can scour the sky day and night. With the number, speed and height-scaling power of our modern planes we can get through the clouds and see all over our globe."

It is precisely because someone did try to grapple with one of these 'things', it is precisely because the 'thing' he tried to grapple with was still stranger and more monstrous than either of the other two thus far sighted, that tragedy for the first time stepped into the story. What had been strange and possibly sinister, became grim!

25

Chapter IV

THE TRAGIC CHASE

THE NEW YEAR of 1948 was only a week old—the second
year of the Disc Era—when Death took his first toll. Before,
however, the baffling tale is plotted out let us remember one
thing of great importance. These 'trespassers'—if we should so
call them—have been scrupulously careful 'to observe the
amenities'. They may have been observing us—or even may be
interested in something other than us—but certainly they have not
pressed their curiosity to impertinent lengths. There is no evidence
that they have ever made any motion toward landing—though one
or two not very reliable reports say they did come near the ground,
they certainly took care to do so when no one was about who might
object. We must repeat, they have always tried to get out of the
way.

It is of the utmost importance that we should never forget this.
And it is of the utmost importance that we should remember that
fact when we are reading this chapter. For tragic as the encounter
proved, the 'encountered', the visitor *did everything, within its remarkable powers, to avoid a contact, to keep clear of complications*.
Though as terrible a monster as any the human eye has ever rested
on, it ran like a hare away from the rash man who pursued it.
That being clear beyond a doubt, now we must have the story.

It is also clear beyond a doubt that the authorities were uneasy.
Of course they were, or they would be unfit to be authorities. They
were caught between two acute anxieties. The first thing was of
course, 'What the Devil is this?' No one is inspired today and
everyone knows it. Today the more informed you are the better
you know that your best and brightest guess peers over the edge
of a blank, black abyss, out of which no one knows what next will
emerge.

The second anxiety of a lively authority in this up-to-date, going-to-pieces world is that no one knows how much the public will stand. What if the wildest phantasy proved true? What if the last thing we are clinging to in the back of our minds—that at least (though God, and inspired prophets, and infallible authorities are all put by public opinion under a cloud) Man is the one thing that matters, at least we are the only persons who can think and act and direct our fate—what if that is untrue? What if there are other creatures as clever, yes, much more clever than we? Now, would the public, the democratic, the 'I am the crown of creation and the master of my destiny' public, would that present-day public stand for that view being squashed and flattened? Again, nobody knows; and that question, of course, is second to none to a democratic politician.

So the authorities have been uneasy and have tried, like all uneasy people in control, to keep a straight face and say as little as possible. But they had to find out. It was on the 7th January 1948 that the New Year brought a present—a possibility of finding out. And the offer was a big one—the biggest ever up to date.

Fort Knox in Kentucky, (famous through the world as the place where the vastest heap of gold ever accumulated in all history used to be kept buried)—Fort Knox was chosen as the centre of the scene of action—and tragedy. This was to be no case where, somewhere off the track, over some quiet countryside, in the night, a couple, or maybe one observer, saw something for a few moments. No, it was to be (as far as the word 'showing' means showing something) it was to be a showdown.

It was just getting on for three in the afternoon—the time when the light is still very good and men fresh and alert. The State police about half-past two had been the first to give the warning and certainly scores of people had already reported seeing something that made the State police call to the Military police as a matter of urgency.

A huge object that shone brightly in the afternoon light was travelling through the sky at a vast speed. And it was evidently making its way toward a big Air Force Field, the Godman Base. The Air Field was then on the alert. And those on watch didn't

27

have to wait long. The Godman Field tower was manned with its leading personnel. The Commanding Officer, Colonel Hix, was in control. He was using his binoculars and they had found their mark. The clouds were broken. Through them appeared Something which proved that warnings sent ahead were in no way exaggerated. The clouds thinned and the whole group of expert and responsible people—as competent a bunch as could be found in all the world—the entire team saw. The object was huge. The size must be estimated. There was not much doubt about it—only that it could not be. But any estimate which was made by ordinary checking seemed to show that it must be, to say the least, 500 feet across. What there was no doubt about—(and this was a new saucer style)—it shot out pulses or blasts of red flame.

But the group in the observation tower were not just going to stand and gape and hope the clouds would clear off and the 'thing' oblige by standing still. It was clear enough that it was going its own sweet way at its own strong gallop. So, not expecting otherwise, the Command had made ready.

Three fighting planes were already up and racing every moment higher to come up with the intruder. Nor had the Command to wait. One of the most wonderful features of modern flying, and what has made for so much of its security, is that the ground controls and commands, and the ships in the sky, can keep in constant touch, in instant communication with each other.

And now the scouts, hidden high above the clouds, began to speak clearly to the whole group in the tower. At least the man in command of the scout fleet of three was now speaking. That was Captain Mantell.

His report was good as far as not being disappointing. But it was grim too. Yes, he had the quarry in view. He was on its tracks. And there had been no exaggeration. It was of 'tremendous size'. It looked, too, as if it were metallic.

Then the voice from the far-up plane went on. "The thing is climbing." The next phase was hopeful. "It is going only half the speed of the pursuit."

Yes, he would try to close in. But after five minutes, when the loudspeaker again took up its tale, it was not so certain. The monster had evidently taken fright. It had shown its mettle—it was now climbing at nearly 400 miles an hour.

When the speaker again addressed the tower group the voice was from one of Mantell's companions. Both he and his fellow plane had seen the object. But they had lost sight of it now and of Mantell. For he had gone on up after it and had disappeared in still higher cloud.

At last, at quarter past three, Mantell's voice was heard again. He was holding on and up. But the thing was still rising above him and might be increasing the gap between them. Still he would track it as far as he could go—he thought he could stand up to 20,000 feet altitude. Then if that didn't bring him at least to a better and a closer view, he would give up. Probably he did. No one knows for certain.

The wreckage of his plane was picked up over a wide area. How he actually met his death no one could say for sure—but dead he was. When his voice could no longer be got on the loudspeaker, the command ordered one of his companions to search upwards. He went not only to 33,000 feet. He swung over hundreds of miles of sky-scape. But there was not a glimmer of the immense thing they had all seen rolling above them.

Fort Knox issued a release on the subject. The Commander, Colonel Hix, was acknowledged to have watched the visitor, which was said to be "unidentified"; and Captain Mantell was declared to have been killed while chasing it. "The rest is silence."

But there was a rumour that at Columbus, Ohio, at the airfield there, as the sun was setting on that fatal day, a disc rushed overhead; and this disc had a big flaming flue-blast trailing out behind it.

So the tragic chase closed with the first saucer casualty. The sacrifice made by the gallant pioneer did not add to our knowledge any more than might have been gleaned from the ground. The observations from the tower showed that the mysterious machine was a new species and may be a new genus of this strange visitation. Before, no disc of that size had been noted—though some may have been as big, but too high to be gauged.

But what none before had shown was this great flare of angry incandescence from the stern. And still there were more to come —to make the whole problem more of a headache—more facts to make the whole thing more credible, less able to be fitted into any, even the most unpleasant, of human explanations. Further, as we shall see in the next chapter, with unabated courage, pilots were ready to tackle and maybe intercept one of these uninvited visitors.

Chapter V

THE PHANTOM HUNT

IT was now the 1st October 1948. Year Two of the discs had been full of inconclusive evidence, some hoaxes, many mistaken sightings such as those of weather balloons, a great deal certainly pointing to something—but to what definite conclusion? No one could say. No one very much wanted to say. For if the clue to the mystery was a secret weapon, why then no one would want to talk about what might be spoilt by talking. If it was 'another Power', there again no one wanted panic started. And if it was something not human at all—why then least of all did anyone want to talk!

People like new things provided they are nice things—and the word 'nice' means that "they must fit in with what I like and not upset my life". No one could help feeling that something so outside our ordinary ways must at the best be unsettling. Our society aims at comfort. Our research is to add to the comfort and pleasure of life. No one could imagine how the discs—the farther off one had to put their base—could in any way add to our comfort— quite the reverse! All the more, then, must those who had to know —the Defence Forces—know. And knowledge kept on coming down from the skies but, wisdom, the power to make sense of the whole thing, that, as usual lingered.

But the case that follows, though it is so important and puzzling, ended, though not in tragedy, yet in further bewilderment. The evening of that first October day had already settled in. It was night over the North Dakota town of Fargo. A National Air Guard Lieutenant named George Gorman, a man of some importance in the city, was coming in from a practice flight in a fighter. He was the last of his group and had just received the O.K. that it was clear and safe for him to land. But looking below his craft he saw, moving very fast, a light between him and the ground. It

31

was moving at an unwise speed considering how close he judged it to be to the earth, for he took it to be the hind light of a plane. He told the landing control below to make sure again that all was clear. They told him there was only one other plane in the district, and as it happened he could pick up its outline—well out of his way. And more, it was nowhere near the patrolling light.

Further, as the light circled about until it was between Gorman and a lighted ground area, Gorman saw no body, no structure of any sort round the light—there was just a flame without a holder, a moving light without anything to move it, or carry it.

The tower control-man caught sight of the light. He had, of course, night-binoculars—so he could see far better than Gorman. But like Gorman he could see just the light and nothing round it.

Then Gorman decided on a bold thing. He was above the light. So he swooped on it. And that apparently caught its wandering attention. It paused and then, quick as a matador with a charging bull, side-stepped. As Gorman swooped past, it slipped off to his right. It was only a foot or so in size, a white globe. He thought it was making for the tower, and he dived at it again.

For twenty minutes this skilful flyer dived and ducked at this queer enigmatic opponent—an opponent who certainly knew how to play the game and who, in boxing terms, could show some pretty footwork. They danced this night sky duet above the air field. Some of the turns made by the light as leader were so sharp and neat that they made Gorman go as black in his consciousness as the night outside. This touch and touch again of the grim danger of blacking-out made Gorman think fast. The thing was behaving humanly, one might say even humourously, but could it be human and flick round corners and make turns like that? Could any human brain stand such spinning and sudden twisting?

That problem of whether human beings can turn as quickly as discs turn is going to rise again. We had best then note it well now. For much may depend upon the answer to that question. The facts of human anatomy are stubborn things. We were not meant to function above a certain rate and pressure and power of spin. Exceed that and you will be lucky, very lucky if you do not find yourself laid out—and perhaps for good.

But when at last Gorman, by a quick stroke, seemed as if he might for a moment actually get in the path of the light, it appeared to lose patience. With its usual unexpected readiness it suddenly swung. But not away—straight on to Gorman. He and the light were now diving right into each other. Gorman then did a dip and the light sailed over him. Perhaps that counted it a point. Gorman thought, however, that he must make another dash for it. Again they came head on. But this time—as it must be owned the discs always seem to do—it took to its good manners and used its full powers—it just hopped right up into the air, as the old Cretan bull-fighters used to leap right over the charging bull.

But Gorman would not let it go. By that time, however, the Thinking Light had tired of playing ball with its rather clumsy human pick-up. He came on panting up behind it. But it, light as Ariel, rushed up to 14,000 feet and then (after Gorman's plane had coughed but got its wind again and taken him to 17,000 feet) the 'Light' shook itself free of its heavy hanger-on, sailed up into the Night and was gone.

This unequalled joint-performance of man-and-mystery, flame-and-fighter plane was watched by quite an audience. To the two men in the tower were added another couple, who had just arrived by plane. This moving body—if it can be called a body—had no trail. And no one heard any sound come from it.

What we can say is that we may be thankful that the brush with the 'Light' did not end as had ended the only other close-up with someone or something coming from above. There, as we have seen, the poor earth-aspirant repeated that very first story of flying, where the rash young Icarus, son of Daedalus, the first inventor of wings-for-men, flew, against his father's orders, too high. His wings disintegrated as their waxen fastenings melted and he fell, to be drowned in the sea which the Greeks later named after him and his disastrous exploit.

Surely it is an absurd, an unscientific approach to anything in the air, to try to run up alongside it, still less to try to run it down!

What is the sense of sending up 'fighters' (planes meant just to down an opponent who otherwise will down you) to tackle a

c

monster of utterly unknown power and speed, and of a size so enormous — some said it was nearly 1,000 feet across — that its very wash might throw to the earth any of our planes?

It was even more ridiculous for one of our fighter planes to try to tackle a light. What can a tiger do about a beam of deadly X-rays? His defence and attack are not in the same world as short-wave radiation. It can kill him without his knowing it. He can do nothing to it. His one chance is to give it a wide berth—unless he can track its source and break up the 'tube' that emits it. There, though, lies a clue, or a possible one, in this last case, of the Light-Chase, the Hunt for a Will o' the Wisp.

One thing will strike anyone who reads this report, or at least one question must arise:— Surely that 'Light' was being 'projected'? There must have been—if the whole thing was not a phantom hunt but a factual hunt — there must have been someone, high aloft, who was directing this little bright 'bait', directing it on the flying field of Fargo to see what the men-minnows in the bottom of the earth-atmosphere pool would do. The 'person' far, far above played with the one 'minnow' that rose.

But—and this is vitally important—though the minnow, like any other mindless minnow, dashed at the bait, and tried to capture it, the high, hidden 'fisherman' was, thank heaven, much more a patient naturalist than a sportsman wanting to land a catch. 'He' played with the poor little creature which was able to swim only as high as the water of its pool extended (and so at 17,000 feet could be let slide back to mud-level). 'He' took care to learn as much as he could of the minnow's power not only of manoeuvre but of mind — tested to see what turns it could take, of what tactics it was capable, what its resistance to strain, what its inventiveness to sudden movement might be.

There is then no escaping the conclusion—as all who were in on that play agreed—that there was an intelligence guiding that 'Light'. That is interesting, if perhaps a little too much so. What is not only interesting but heartening is that that intelligence showed itself considerate. It wanted to learn about us *and* it was not only clever in the way it did so, but considerate.

As to the tragic Mantell case—again what else could be

expected? This huge thing, this monstrous sky-master, scuttled away from the silly gnat that kept on rushing after it. The huge space-ship succeeded in shaking off the two other fliers (sent up in fighters) without doing the frail little gnats a penn'orth of harm. No one knows how near Mantell got. The current explanation is that as he had no oxygen with him; above 20,000 feet he 'blacked-out' (as was to be expected) and that while he was in a swoon, his plane got out of control. A crash from that height has been due to that cause. But Mantell may have got right into the danger zone—and by that is meant, right near the wash of this terrible thing's inconceivable engines.

We shall find that question with us to the end of this enquiry. The next chapter gets down to it—or up to it. And Chapter IX tries to collect and order all the deductions so far made.

They do seem to point to one thing—these 'ships' are as peculiar in their power as in their shape. They do command some sort of prodigious energy, the like of which is just under the horizon of our speculation. Now if a silly boy is rash enough to swim near the screws of an ocean liner when they begin to turn he will certainly be sucked down and drowned. The captain of the liner cannot help that—you must keep clear of that wash and suction.

There are already to hand two reports from observers who say they watched discs flying over a forest on a still day; and what struck them most was that the tops of the trees, as the discs passed high above them, twisted and lashed as if a small typhoon were passing over them. Finally there was a report that Mantell's plane-fragments did show signs of such 'handling'. There were grooves in the metal, driven right through it. 'Machine gun fire?' But what in the name of the unknown would a space ship of that size be doing manned with such archaic arquebuses as machine guns? Does a modern battleship, powered with turbines and dynamos, arm itself with bows and arrows and so beat off attack? No, taking for granted the size and power of this, the greatest of all the sky-visitors yet viewed with any accuracy, we can only conclude one thing. These searchers and explorers from the sky are considerate—indeed there is every reason to suppose that they are wise as they are clever, as gentle as they are ingenious.

In this case they were escaping so fast that they thought they had left the 'gnats' safely behind. Then one got close enough—close enough to hit that intense 'wake' of discharging atom-force, radiation energy, needed to drive this artificial island up into the air-less sky, out into space, maybe. The rods of force, the hets of energy flashing out from that stern would be more penetrating than any bullet, than any jet from an oxy-acetylene torch (which drives its darting tongue of flame through steel as if through butter). The accident would be hopelessly unavoidable—the kind of pathetic thing when a poor wild animal steps on a live wire and is instantaneously killed.

Such then are the conclusions, the only reasonable conclusions with which the evidence leaves us—evidence which we cannot set aside or brush away. Yet something hopeful, something constructive comes out of these two key-reports. First and foremost we need not, we must not, become panicky. The visitors have behaved with consideration and correctitude. Think how you would plan to conduct yourself with the utmost decorum if you were visiting another world—or another country with which you found it hard to communicate. You could not find a sounder method of approach than that which these strangers have used towards us. We can then watch and wait, and above all not be belligerent toward those who have shown no abruptness with us. We can conclude that the fighter-plane approach is both silly—for it was quite unpractical—and dangerous, for surely it would be hard not to misunderstand it. If every time I go into a field a bull charges me, I may be forgiven for assuming that he does not want to establish friendly relations with me, or even to study impartially my behaviour and habits.

But what can we do? Are we simply to wait sitting on the ground, dumb and mainly blind? No one likes being looked down on and being spied upon by someone above, least of all the creature that has just learnt to fly. That is why the next reports are so important. For they carry us a step further—not merely do they give us more evidence about the discs—they show us a new approach to them.

Chapter VI

THE ROCKET OUTRACED

THE time had now come when the ground began to gain on the air. Up to this point we all thought, Well you must get abreast of the Thing, on the level with 'it'. That, we see, proved harder and harder, until we have to face the conclusion that it is impossible as well as quite possibly very dangerous. The old instruction for over-curious little boys when being taken round a power house, comes to mind, "Look, but don't touch!"

As it happens the ground has great advantage over the air. From the ground we can make more accurate observations than from a plane. The theodolite allows for that. A common instrument, an essential part of every crew of surveyors, with its telescope and its equipment for reading-off heights of objects and their computed distance, it is just what every disc sighter would like to have his eye to when one of these objects crosses the sky. And so quite early in this three-year hunt of the sky it befell that a surveyor team, equipped with their theodolite, set up and ranged, got their big chance. It was again at Boise, Idaho, where the hunt had started in June 1947, that on the 20th February 1948 the Idaho Power Company had a crew in operation. They were actually working at a small place called Emmet and it was to the paper, *The Emmet Messenger*, that Mr. E. G. Hall—who actually made the theodolite observation—gave his account. He was standing ready when one of his colleagues pointed out something in the sky. Hall ranged on it. He got it, but had the greatest difficulty in keeping it in the field of vision, because of its speed.

Still he felt sure of the following facts:— Its height was only some 4,000 feet, its size that of a smallish plane. Along its back-edge was no trail of fume. *But* there was a 'fuzziness' there, 'like whipped cream'. (Now that is important, for it would seem to show some form of energy which, escaping into our atmosphere, vaporises in a peculiar way). It was gleaming white. Sound? 'It was as silent as a gull'. As it got near a hill the onlookers, for there were two of Hall's companions viewing it, expected it to go over a cloud bank, measured as being some 2,000 feet high. But the disc chose to go under. So it must have been very silent not to have been heard when rushing headlong so near the ground. A number of other people saw it. The time was ideal, just after 1 p.m. So this is the first known gauged, theodolite-measured, properly reported, 'viewing'. This is the first time that a trained eye using a 'transit' was able to 'scan' a 'visitor'. Mr. Hall maintains that he saw no cockpit nor engine-mounts. It was as non-committal as a white plate flung quoit-wise through the sky, and, in spite of its rush, as silent as the grave.

We had to wait for another year—to be exact 14 months—before we got another theodolite ranged with its observer on another disc. This is not to be wondered at. The chances cannot be very high. Probably not more than 400 sightings all told have been made of discs—though some reliable people who have tried to make that sort of check-up think that it is nearer 800. But for things that show up for a matter of seconds, in far the greater number of cases, what else could be expected? There is seldom time even to get a camera. But, as it happened, when the chance came in April 1949, it was splendid. If anyone had asked, he could not have been given a more perfect set-up. Ideal observation conditions, model crew and a faultless performance by the observed —by the discs themselves.

Take the observation conditions first, for they are basic. Of one thing we can have no doubt. These 'things' usually fly high, very high indeed and at very high speed. So, if the weather conditions are not of the best, what chance has one of making anything like a satisfactory observation? Anyone can test that for himself. Look out when next you hear a plane. Most of the time it is a sound and very often it stays that—till it dies away into the distance. And these 'things' very seldom make a sound. So first and foremost you must have an area of very fine weather. That means a desert, where thin, dry air is the rule and a hard blue sky, deep blue, is the day-by-day 'ceiling'. That is why the desert is chosen for upper-air observations.

When after the war the captured German super-rockets were found, and brought to the United States for testing, there was clearly only one place to choose for this testing—the great South West Desert of America that stretches through New Mexico and the other arid states of Arizona and Nevada. There, safely, had been kept and tried out the terrible secret of the Atom Bomb. Besides, in that wilderness there are so few people, so scanty an occupation, that it is safe to throw things into the sky and let them fall back, without risking the life or limb of district dwellers. So the crews, to send off and to watch these super-rockets, were sent to a place that has been much written up now—White Sands, New Mexico.

The results, too, have been remarkable. We have learnt much about the upper atmosphere, much that was very strange. 'Air' from up there has been captured and brought down bottled. There is not room here to go into the remarkable finds that have been made. The rockets have penetrated into heights, up into rarefied strata of atmosphere, where no instrument of man has yet gone, and have brought back masses of fascinating information. Nevertheless the most remarkable thing that has as yet come to hand was no part of the research 'project'. It came (there seems no possible doubt) because, being highly intelligent, 'it' thought it, too, might look on and study with us—and study us and our study-tools.

Commander R. B. McLaughlin is an expert. All his professional life he has been specialising in missile study. That led of course to work on guided missiles and rockets. He was put in charge in 1946 of the division of such research at the White Sands Rocket-Ground as had to be covered by the Navy. One of the crews of observers for whom he was jointly responsible was out on a day of unusually good conditions for observation—in the month of April. They were working nearly sixty miles away from the actual Rocket-Ground. For they were watching with a theodolite and doing other scientific checking of a weather-balloon they had sent up. But the theodolite-man of the crew got his attention side-tracked. Naturally the rest had seen 'it', crossing by the balloon. It was a 'standard disc'—there could be no doubt—a 'moderate' model, i.e. about 100 feet across. But there its moderation ended, sharply. For it was nearly 60 miles up! And its speed was even worse—some 18,000 miles an hour! But its power of acceleration was the real 'headache'. For when it had made its pass at the balloon, as seems common with the species, it made a dart up—to its native level? Whether that was its aim or no, of the speed at which it made this sudden kick up there could not be a doubt. It would be exerting, the experts had no doubt, a pressure on any-one inside equal to the pressure of gravity being increased twenty times!!!

We shall be coming across that difficulty—or insight—as to what can be inside these discs—again and again. For it is crucial. No man could stand it for a moment. That jerk, that sudden increase of pressure, would press us to death. Only insects could stand being suddenly compressed like this—that is, the inertia of their bodies suddenly made to meet the battering-ram impact of the walls they are against or the floor they are standing on, suddenly boosting them ahead. The team had a full minute to watch it. That gives trained men with their instruments quite a long while to see and to reflect. Then the white discus high up in the deep blue did the usual disappearance act. It was gone.

Incidentally, as these machines are flat and so very disc-shaped that may account for these sudden disappearances. They turn edge-on and so they are gone in a flick. After all, the rings of Saturn (which are an obvious feature for every amateur astrono-mer to find for himself) were lost again and again by their dis-coverers. (See Chapter XIV). For the rings are actually so thin, (though so striking when seen 'full-face') that they have only lately, with modern telescopes, been picked up when their edges are pointed at us.

It happened that the Navy Chief, McLaughlin himself, was not present. He trusted his team, of course; but he himself had not seen the disc.

However, a month later the disc saw that this oversight on their part was repaired. This time the Commander was 'viewing'. A rocket had just been sent up — and he and another officer were standing gazing up to where it had just disappeared from ordinary sight as it rushed up to the limits of the atmosphere. Then the other officer pointed out to the Commander what he took to be the rocket coming home. They both saw it, as did a third officer. It was white and going at far too slowly a pace for a homing projectile. It began to mend its pace, passed over their heads and the lookers-on thought with dismay that it was going to come to earth close to one of the few ranch houses in that desolate area. Then it changed its mind, put on a prodigious burst of speed and was lost behind some hills. Still they thought it was their missile and the Commander at once got on the telephone to warn the supposed senders that he was sure their send-up had strayed and was going to pay a very unwelcome visit to someone who, being outside the testing range, ought to have been safe from that form of molestation. The information was hardly passed on before it was denied —denied by the reassurance given by the big bump they all heard —the bump that signals that the rocket has come down safely in its allotted ground.

So the thing that the Commander and his colleagues had viewed must have been—what? The only answer seemed to be 'a disc', and one up to its usual dance. There was the 'saunter', the stroll, say about 20 or 30 miles high. There was the fabulous—and to any man on board such a craft, anything larger than a mouse, the fatal—burst of acceleration. Yet, with all that there was no evidence of the burst of speed leading to a burst of gas, a trail to mark the increase of kick. No, as with the discs of this sort, the object suddenly shot like a thing out of a gun, but gave not a clue as to what drove it to such a break-away.

So when one month later still—in June—the discs looked in again at the testing ground (though again it was a team that saw them, and not the Commander), he felt that, even less than at the first sighting, could he dismiss the evidence brought him. The first upper-air missile had been a job of the Army's. This one was a Navy job for the Commander's own division of the Forces. The missile had not disappeared when two 'Sky Inspectors' arrived. No one saw them come. The observers simply found that a brace

41

of discs—or at least platters—had appeared alongside, and what is stranger still, were running up alongside the climbing missile. Perhaps they were the smallest ever seen. They were thought to be less than two feet across. Then one dashed through the wake of the rocket and came out beside its companion on the other side. Still stranger, now they were together, they started racing each other. And they made such speed that they left the rocket behind them, going up and away—the usual exit.

Nor did the Commander have to rest with the evidence of only this one team. From nearly a dozen of the look-out posts, which are placed at distances round the huge field—miles in length—to keep posted as to where a stray missile may fall—from one after another came the telephone reports—the twins had been viewed in their amazing, and, till then, unprecedented flight.

Chapter VII

'PROJECT SAUCER' AND PUBLIC OPINION

MEANWHILE what was authoritative opinion doing about all this? We saw at the very beginning of the story that three factors made the fibres of this strange tale. The first were the actual experiences of a number of skilled men, trained in accurate observation of aerial craft and sky-phenomena. This sum of most valuable opinion and findings has grown.

You can rub off and brush away the reports of good-hearted and honest lookers-on, who may mistake a meteorological balloon or a meteor as an unknown, original air-craft. But you cannot get rid of the evidence of men who are trained to observe and who are on their own ground. These men do not want publicity—quite the reverse. They do not want to see things that are odd. They are neither credulous nor fanciful. As that most capable of critics and sceptics, the great logician John Stuart Mill, laid down as a basic law of evidence and of the attempts to rebut it, "We must remember that men are more likely to be right in what they affirm than in what they deny". For the principle is based on the fact which anyone can prove for himself—that hallucination (however common it may be) is less common, far less common, than ignorance. There are in the universe, any sensible man knows, far more things that he has never seen than those things which he has imagined were there and which were not there.

In addition to the trained observers, the first-class look-outs, there were others. Not only were there those people who never seem to observe accurately, and who always embroider what, in Sir W. S. Gilbert's immortal phrase, is called the "bald and unconvincing narrative." There is the utter 'hoaxer'—that exasperating person who gets his sense of superiority from taking in people—the man who wants to be talked about, even though he is ruining the quality of reliability among average people who tell the truth. Such people

43

are the spiritual descendants of the man who burnt down that wonder of the ancient world, the Temple of Artemis at Ephesus, and gave as his reason that now he would be talked about. Naturally the discs have seemed an opportunity to such people. Their reports have been dug into, and most of them have crumpled up.

But the existence of such creatures does make the work of finding out what actually happens doubly difficult. And it does go some considerable way to explain why responsible men—(and especially those who have to carry most responsibility, the officials of the Defence Forces and of the Government)—have 'leant over backwards' to keep the story from getting premature approval; and have exposed the evidence to examination again and again in the hope that in the end it might all be fitted into known or likely types of experience.

For that is the third thread in our story—the official story, what the authorities said about the saucers. Now this story by itself is one as complex as any psychological novel ever written. Yet we should not be surprised at that. As was said at the start, this is not an easy subject. And, as we all know to our cost in daily anxiety, this is not the time when you can say all you have on your mind. It is not a time when mankind is behaving with such world-wide rationality and respect for reason that we can give all our attention to things that may be coming from outside our world or from sources that are not official.

We must repeat, America is the freest country in the world. Except during a war you may ask about anything and expect an answer. That is because the Press is so powerful. And the Press has power to push its probes so vigorously because the American Public wants news almost as much as it wants fresh food. The President is regularly quizzed; his aides are cross-questioned, even on their private affairs. Even Mrs. Mary Baker Eddy, when regarded by many as almost superhuman, had to give an interview, and a long and intimate one, to the Press. The American Public therefore expects its officials to tell it, in reason, what they are doing and what is happening in their respective fields.

We have seen the first reaction of the Armed Forces' authorities in the Northwest corner of the States, where the discs problem first became of nation-wide concern. The usual official line was to say that the evidence was far too poor to permit anything but the conclusion that these stories were inconclusive. That was fair enough. You need a lot of evidence to lift stories out of the rut of ordinary explanations into a class by themselves—'inexplicable'. Besides, look at the map. The Northwest of America is now a frontier as tight and nervous as those old festering frontiers which in Europe, with only a few miles separating camps of counter-armed men, used to make frontier incidents a continual sleep-spoiler for weary diplomats and jumpy Foreign Offices. The plane had made frontiers both ridiculous and doubly dangerous. So that display out to sea which the citizens of Portland and Seattle looked up at on that Fourth of July fiesta day in 1947 must have seemed, to Defence Force men, anything but delightful. Could it be a big and sombre neighbour looking over the coast, looking down at the great open areas of the big Northwest?

But as the reports grew, two things did grow clearer, if not more comprehensible. First they could not be dismissed, they must be quizzed and sifted and criticised. The second also called for a little more openness. If they would stand up to examination at all, then they would perhaps prove themselves not to be the most pressing of perils. Perhaps, if the proofs held up, they would carry the whole question—strange as that might seem—right outside present political controversies and international tensions.

Whatever the reason, the fact is clear. On the last day but one of the Year One of the Discs, 30th December 1947, the decision was ready to be launched. Project Saucer was to be set up. There was to be a central authority, equipped with experts—astro-physicists, electronic experts, and meteorologists. Radar, as well as the telescope, was to be at the service of these judges and searchers. Even that wonderfully efficient instrument for discovery, the Federal Bureau of Investigation, an invaluable service for disclosing hoaxers, was asked to aid the Project.

The first summaries that were issued were clear and hopeful. The greater part of the reports had been satisfactorily disposed of. But it was admitted that a residuum, a core of hard fact, seemed to be left. So the moral, as the issue of these findings gave it, was definite and lucid. There seemed to be no rift between the public and its representatives. There was a free exchange of news. The public brought in its 'viewings'. The Project questioned, enquired, weighed; and then gave the finder and the rest of the public what it estimated the value of raw material to be. And it was allowed—a conclusion with which a very sensible private person must agree—that as there were unidentified air objects wandering about which could be at present attributed to no known source, why then "constant vigilance" was needed not only by those on the Project but by the Public. Please report to the authorities anything you see as soon as you see it.

There were also helpful pieces of information: (i) Telling the Public what they might mistake for 'Unidentified Air Objects', and (ii) What the Unidentified Objects had been said to look like—the four types we now know: The discs; the long, black wingless tube; giant 'balloons', and balls of light. The report ended with a friendly note. "The Saucers are not a joke. Neither do they give cause for alarm on the part of the population."

Here is a frank facing up to an exciting mystery. There is no ground for misgiving. There is evidence of a mystery. There is the chance of making some very interesting finds. That is the kind of relationship one expects to exist between the Government of a free country and its free constituents. Life is an adventure and has risks; but if people are left free and given carefully tested information as it comes to hand, they can face surprises and make constructive responses.

At this point the Project itself became a mystery. Throughout, the Air Force had said that, to the best of its knowledge, there were no such things as discs and it gave in March 1950 a definite denial that the Air Force itself was engaged on any work that could be taken for the kind of thing that appeared in the newspaper descriptions. Nothing was being made for secret missiles or space-ships that could at all resemble discs.

Yet the reports went on. Thus far, no one summarised the story as a whole. In May 1949 the big-circulation illustrated, *The Saturday Evening Post*, did, it is true, issue an article that ran in two parts in successive issues. The survey of the evidence was written by a very competent reporter who had gone round and collected not only stories, but also the opinions of various Air Force Commands and Intelligence Officers. The conclusion was that the public might rest assured that there was very little in the whole thing, and pretty certainly nothing.

But while this clear statement was being read with some assurance by hundreds of thousands of readers, the Air Force issued a statement on its own—the statement containing the remark that there were cases of unidentified craft having been sighted aloft and that these cases indicated that vigilance was the proper attitude not only for official look-out men but also by the public.

So once more the issue seemed in suspense, literally hanging in the air. And, if human evidence could be trusted at all, the phenomena were finding more and more occasions to hang out over the heads of surprised persons. What, however, was becoming clear was that the public mind and the professional mind were now tending to change places. At the start of Project Saucer, at the very end of 1947, the experts had been a bit ahead of public opinion. The experts, we see, had declared that something might be there. On the whole, after the first burst of excitement, and a lag in fresh stories, the public—as is generally the case—began to think less well of the somewhat stale sensation. The big magazines that people look to to summarise, order and give judgment on a series of scattered items—whether of pure research or what we used to call Natural History observations—all of these organs of considered judgment kept quiet.

While we have seen what a wide-ranging magazine such as *The Saturday Evening Post* had to say, the refusal of the big magazines and the powerful, acute dailies to touch the story with any seriousness, undoubtedly influenced the educated. For instance, *Harper's Magazine*, second to none as a fine monthly of the old school, chose to take a big risk with its reputation by giving a first place to the astounding theory of the Hebrew scholar Dr. Velikovsky—that the Hebrew account of Joshua's sun standing still to convenience Irael in winning a battle was astronomically true—the earth had stood still, had been brought to a standstill by a comet which

47

was on its way to become the planet Venus—which, incidentally, had not existed before that comparatively very modern date!

Yet *Harper's,* which would generously extend its aegis over such a magnificently tall story—one which the astronomers and sidereal historians refused to sponsor—would not so serve the saucers. But surely it is of more interest to an American whether or no super-airships are over their country, than whether (to convenience some tribes in the Bronze age—and profoundly inconvenience the rest of the globe's inhabitants by the cataclysm the stopping of the world is said to have caused), the Sun once paused over proto-historic Palestine?

There was no doubt here a pretty play between the two horns of that great bull, Democracy, the horn of the public, the source of all authority, and the horn of the politician, the expression of all authority. A Free Citizen in a Free Democracy may rightly be as afraid of embarrassing his Free Government, as the Unfree Subject of an Unfree State may naturally fear offending the Government that controls him by Force. As long as the discs could be earthly—and unearthly notions are really not at all native to the American mind—then alas, who in the world could produce them if not America? Only one person, only one Number One.

So here again was a dilemma:— Either these discs are ours—and that of course, while reassuring, is one of those reassurances about which we naturally want to say as little as possible. This view has been emphatically stated. The clearest, most definite assertion of it has been given time and again—one of the last of his statements was made on 11th May 1950—by the well-known columnist and commentator Henry J. Taylor, addressing a large audience in Los Angeles. In spite of the official denials, this public man says the saucers are real and *are* U.S.A. Secret Weapons. Or, and this is the other horn of the dilemma, pressing us to silence—or they come from the only other possible source. If that is so, what can be done but keep quiet and wait; and hope that an answer is known to someone, an answer so complete that it would be madness to ask for it before it speaks decisively for itself and on our behalf?

So much for the public and their wish to be silent—if the discs are earth-born. The other horn of the Democratic bull has also equal reason for wanting to pull itself in and keep its own counsel. The Government of a fully Democratic State must live in a kind of humorous fear (or perhaps, in humility, it would call the feeling by the old-fashioned but stately name 'godly fear') of its queer master the public. An oligarchy can thumb its nose at the people— "Everything from the people: nothing for the people" is its motto; and it tells them flatly that they can govern through the naturally born governors but never on their own. But a true democracy cannot. The President of the United States is in one way the most powerful man in the world; but only so long as he knows he is not—that is to say only if he knows that he must daily accept, silently and cheerfully, jibes and attacks, from which the least powerful citizen in the whole country could and would take refuge in the law to protect and vindicate him.

So, with discs aloft, it is natural for both horns to say, each to the other, "Gentlemen, you go first. You probe—there is no one to stop you". Well then, is the Government fibbing quite heavily when it says that it, itself, knows nothing of earth-launched saucers in the sky? The quizzing has gone on now right up to the Presidential entourage and the President's aides have said frankly they know nothing and that, on their word, they do not believe the President does either.

That brings us to a further development of Governmental Responsibility in a Democracy. No man can be a politician unless he knows by a kind of intuition what people will stand and stand for. In the old safe world in which the American Founding Fathers built their noble Palace of the People, the foundations were clear and firm. You knew the kind of weather that the good sense of the electorate would have to endure. Since those days moral earthquakes have shaken the assurance of free mankind. From Physics saying that anything may happen tomorrow, through Biology beginning to mutter, "But of course you know, we've *proved* men are not equal and quite a lot are too stupid even to be taught"—on to the wastes of Psychology, where human character seems to dissolve in a web of vague emotions and will is merely a figment —why Science today, which was once the free man's friend and

49

D

almost his patient beast of burden, looks more like the phantom dog that the man took for a walk and while in the wood it grew into a tiger—and its poor little master came back home 'inside'.

That then is the chief problem of the Peoples' Rulers today. Can men stand the truth, now that the truth gets stranger and stranger? For instance, just as an example, if you or I were President of the United States and we happened to think—though without absolute certainty—that what was up in the air, as well as being partly men's mistaken opinions of natural things, might have here and there, mixed in it off and on, something even more unsettling than a messenger from "Mr. Number One of the Other Ideology"—what would we do about it? Why, in the name of common sense and sanity, we would wait, the sovereign recipe of every wise ruler.

There is in time of peace no censorship in the United States nor any sign that it would ever be possible. To the old adage, "Who guards the guardian?" free people add the rider "Who censors the censor?"

What then would a wise ruler do who felt uncertain in his own mind of two vital and, when combined, very awkward facts—

(i) That there might be a piece of news that would be beyond anything that men have ever had to stand as yet, hanging over their heads;

(ii) That the people are already as nervy — in these wars-of-nerves—as they have any right to be asked to be—and rather more so.

There are two ways of keeping news back till you are quite sure of it, can define it, can say what it will do and what it cannot do. The first is of course censorship and is, we see, out of the question in peace time. The second is the non-violent way; like most non-violence it is better than the "clamp down" and the "gag"—if you have time to let it work. This second way, too, is one which the United States accepts naturally.

It is the debunking joke. It has been used with great success on that other shocking subject for fifty years and more—the subject of Psychical Research and the discovery of Extra-sensory Perception. You say to the person who begins to show an interest—which you feel he may not have the balance to handle—"What, you taking an interest in that sort of thing! Of course it intrigues shallow minds, emotional, uneducated persons. But, you, with a college degree, of course you don't support those silly collections of stories, those feeble little columns of figures, against the vast sane scientific opinion of the experts!"

A brilliant controversialist opened one of his most telling counter-attacks with the wise and strategic words, "It is hard to answer a sneer". To which wisdom we may add the anthropological observation:— That it is even harder to resist the offer of a cultured friend to get one back into the good graces of the educated, good graces which one's rash and untutored interest in evidence of which they do not approve is in danger of forfeiting for ever.

Excommunication is the most powerful engine man has ever had in his hand. The Greeks, clever as any race, would, however, rather die than be sent into exile. Adam Smith, Father of Economics, says that what drives men to suicide is not loss of goods, or even of health, but loss of their fellows' approval.

Enough has been said to indicate at least a reason why the Government in America may be acting as it is and why the public has done much the same—both have waited, and, like the Tar Baby, for quite a long time, have "gone on saying nuffing". Indeed the Government, as expressed through the expert and official Air Force, have said the subject is closed. 'Project Saucer' probably closed in September 1949. Certainly on the 27th December in that year the Air Force declared that all the cases that had been submitted had been disposed of, as having natural causes.

But the silence of the Press, the well-informed Press, as the silence of the Government deepened into totality, began to have whispers in it. Local papers and small magazines had carried on a gallant attempt to win general attention. It was like blowing a whistle in a soundproof chamber—your cheeks swell, your ear remains unaware.

Then a New York Magazine of standing dared to stand out. *True* is a fine monthly, which issues articles on 'true topics', of adventure, discovery and crime-detection, all well-documented and very well told. *True* decided to take the plunge. It took the greatest care. Were there secrets which ought patriotically not even to be asked about? *True* was certain it was not going to foul any of these defence lines. Then why the silence? For the facts, the data, *True* knew (as every other patient collector, unheld by prejudice must know) that they were true.

There could only be one explanation: the Government and the subject authorities were waiting, waiting until "may" became "must". They were waiting because they honestly doubted how much the public could stand, if the ultimate explanation of the data proved to be true. After all, twelve years ago two famous men of similar name, H. G. Wells, the author, and Orson Welles, the actor, were jointly and innocently responsible for a very queer little anthropological reaction. Wells the elder's story *The War of The Worlds* (in which Martians come to earth) was radio-dramatised by Welles the younger. The story is good, if dated. The 'putting on' was competent. The present writer heard it without warning. The result was odd. Some people scattered about the country actually thought that the news was true and began to make plans to leave town! When this little success was repeated in South America the acknowledgement of its skill was even more spontaneous, to the point of acute embarrassment—for there some of the public attacked the studio for giving so convincing a performance!!

It has often been suggested that the whole of the United States trembles on the edge of such panic. The answer to that is that when the Atom Bomb came, and not more than four years after there stamped in, on the heels of the first fury, the Hydrogen, or Hell Bomb, the people of the United States did what? They continued in their lawful occasions and occupations—they sighed quite a lot—they thought it was a pity and a shame—they went on feeding Europe; believing, certainly kindly and probably wisely, that fed men are less likely to be mad and murderous than men unfed. But are these the acts of men on the edge of madness? Madness and panic are composed of wilder notions.

So *True* got a first-rate reporter—Major Donald Keyhoe (retired), long versed in Air-research. The magazine sent off to the world in consequence as a New Year's message—it came out just after Christmas 1949—its and his considered summary and judgment.

There was no cause for alarm, but much for keen interest. No power on earth could have made these things. The United States was safe in its air supremacy. They were no more and no less than some kind of outer-space phenomena.

That did however upset quite a number of officials, who felt it was going much too far; if not evidentially, then as a matter of discretion. The much-tried public was bound to be upset. And as when people are upset by anything from an earthquake to a twinge of conscience they blame the Government, why, of course it would be bad for politics, bad for 'Business'—(the Stock Exchange is notoriously easy to discourage)—and bad for peace, progress and prestige. But the 'Sovereign People' was not upset. On the contrary, it appeared to be interested, entertained, and even to a certain extent amused.

As said before, the Air Force denied that it had any hand in such contraptions, if indeed they existed. To help that strong doubt to hatch into a conviction in the minds of the public, the Air Force released the files they had collected of cases reported. They maintained that these reports and the rebuttals of them showed that there was nothing to go on enquiring about.

Others who viewed the lists of cases felt that some of the answers, though they might satisfy an Air Official, left the unofficial mind still open, still questioning. Among these students of the new 're-leased material' was Major Donald Keyhoe, and he was certain that the case was anything but closed. To support Major Keyhoe's belief there came to hand, through his efforts, the complete statement and comments of Commander McLaughlin U.S.N. on what had been seen in April, May and June at White Sands, New Mexico.

This, published in the March issue of *True*, was the second great contribution made by this candidly courageous magazine toward letting the public know. And the discs did their bit too! For that breezy month of March—which is by the way the month of Mars, who in his early history was not a god of war but of the first springing month of the year—March 1950 marked an outburst of sightings. They had been sighted fairly frequently through the first two months from Pennsylvania to Texas. And out at sea a plane over the Pacific reported that for five minutes it had a saucer as a companion, but that the saucer tired of the plane's ambling gait and took off at a speed which was utterly beyond anything the plane could command.

The 1st February held a wonderful show — the biggest so far —for the people of Tucson, Arizona. Waiting till dusk, and then making the run, with fire streaming from it, at what was judged to be an altitude of 30,000 feet, the object swooped right over the city. Reaching that position it paused. The trail of smoke that came from it cleared. For a moment there came a burst of black smoke, then the smoke became a light stream again, as off the object went at terrific speed.

A B.29 was just leaving the ground. The radio operator of the Air Force Base control tower asked him to pursue. In vain. All he could say was that the object was making for California, would be there soon—and then? Then no doubt it would take, as they all seem to take, to the sea. Hundreds saw the thing. One citizen said it swayed about so he thought it was a large plane on fire. But no planes were missing. *The Tucson Daily Citizen* carefully collected the reports and next day it asked why on the following afternoon, detachments of the Air Force spent hours stretching vapour trails over the city. The paper remarked that these efforts were not in the least like the trail left by the 'Thing'. But the Associated Press carried no report of this, and news-casters didn't get it.

Three weeks later, right down at the tip of Florida, at Key West, high up (some thought it must have been at heights only a rocket plane could reach) there was again a sudden appearance, a pause or a hover, and then a dash away that made any idea of pursuit hopeless.

But the most remarkable and perhaps the most significant report came from the naval base which Chile keeps right down on the continent of Antarctica to claim her right to that desolate hub of Polar land. Commander Augusto Orrego reported that the discs had been wheeling above his most lonely station. It was, he said, during the bright Antartic night.

"They were one above the other, turning at tremendous speeds". (There may be something very important in that observation.

54

Why, will be suggested in Chapter IX—'The Craft and their Power'.)

Commander Orrego declared "We have photographs to prove what we say" and then added the sad subtraction, "But they are the property of the Chilean Navy and not at present for publication."

Then came a day in March that the town of Farmington, New Mexico, will never forget. Scores of people witnessed the show. It began at 10.30 a.m. and lasted till 11.30 a.m.—a good time of day and a long space of time for seeing. And plenty to see—both seers and seen. The 'seen' were discs and they shot in singles and also in coveys over the town at prodigious speeds.

The advertising manager of *The Farmington Daily Times*, who was with five business men, saw, with them, a mass of these discs go over. They tended to 'flutter'. Then other spectators—for scores were now on the watch—saw one come over low and it was red—an unusual saucer complexion. Boddy, the advertising manager, said he and his friends thought there were no less than 100 craft in the flock they saw go over. The red saucer, which was the only one that was thought to be at a moderate height, was said, observers vouched, to have got from horizon to horizon in three seconds.

On the day of the Equinox, to mark the beginning of the summer side of things, an air-liner crew when near Stuttgart, Arkansas, saw a disc (remarkable for the fact that, as it pulled round in a grand curve—which would have blacked-out any human inside it) flashing a blue-white light. Was it signalling? It had ports on its lower side and they had that odd, canny glow-glare that we have met before in the case of Captain Chiles when the great black tube rushed past him and his colleague as they piloted their passenger-plane.

On the Stuttgart case, described above, United Press based a definite report-story. The two observers, Captain Adams and First Officer Anderson both made statements. They added to their report their opinion given as a conviction—"Firmly believe the flying saucer we saw was secret experimental type aircraft—not a visitor from outer space".

Well, report is one thing and belief arising from an external inspection is another.

The two men added, "We know that the Air Force has denied that there is anything in this flying saucer business! But we are both experienced pilots and we are not easily fooled".

Certainly, not by the fact that something was there. But did it show its 'port-clearance papers'? Did it tell them it was made-on-earth or where on earth it was made? Of course it did not.

And so the stories grew in numbers, as the days increased in length and the chances of upper-air observation improved.

The Californian coast had a fine crop. At Laguna Beach, a well-known seaside resort, a covey was seen to go overhead and as usual turn out to sea and vanish from sight.

By May it was time for one of the 'Polls of Public Opinion' to report on the condition of American conviction. On 20th May George Gallup, Director of the American Institute of Public Opinion, issued his findings. These showed one thing—that the public was neither frightened nor sceptical. In 1947 most people when questioned had said "Fake and Fraud", "Hoax and Nonsense".

This time to the question, "What do you think they are?" 23 per cent. said they were Secret Weapons in trial stage or pretty nearly ready. 6 per cent. said "New kind of plane." 3 per cent. "From Russia;" 5 per cent. "From another planet or star;" 94 per cent. "had heard about them". Only 22 per cent. thought they were hoax or illusion.

We may now close this Chapter " 'Project Saucer' and Public Opinion" by adding that when the Dean of Science Editors was asked in May what he thought of the saucers, and was reminded that in the Summer of 1947 he had put them down in the big waste-paper basket of unsubstantial anomalies, labelled 'Hallucination'. he smiled and conceded that the evidence was now good enough to haul up the saucers again out of that oubliette. He thought they were a secret weapon. To the rather innocent rejoinder of his guest —"But that has been so strongly denied," he smiled again, "You know we of the news world have a phrase for that sort of thing," he said, "We call it 'corroborative denial'!"

Chapter VIII

THE WHENCES?

THE authorities may not be using the peculiar method which Polonius cited: "By indirections find directions out". As one of the early passages remarked in the 'Saucer' publications, instructing possible witnesses when the Project was in action. There is nothing to guide human judgment but probabilities. No one can say absolutely that something did not happen. When then can you be sure it has happened? And that point as the paper went on to show—at which probability becomes full certainty—for you —is ruled by you.

There are three degrees of probability for all of us. The first is moderate and may be called Probability of Argument. You cannot be at all sure; but you believe, from what you know that a case could be made—till your opponent can upset it with further evidence as yet unknown to you.

The second may be called Probability of Action—you have reached the point when you are willing not merely to argue, but to act on what you know; you are ready to assume that what you have found is sufficiently proved and points sufficiently to a certain conclusion; and from that conclusion you go on to collect more evidence.

The third is a still further degree of assurance—and we must own it is rarely arrived at in anything but such pure sciences as Physics and Astronomy—sciences which deal with what we used to call dead matter, and now prefer to name the inorganic, those forms and objects that seem to be quite lifeless, quite unconscious. This, the third and highest Probability—which most people, somewhat unwisely, call practical certainty—is Probability of Demonstration. You can account by your explanation for all the evidence that has come to light and been brought to hand. But of course you can never be sure that there is not another explanation that might not cover the facts just as well.

Then what do you do? What has the scientist nearly always done? He has used something which he calls rather ambitiously, the Law of Parsimony. That in ordinary English simply means that the simplest explanation is always to be trusted. But that of course assumes that Nature is at base quite simple. Now that *may* be so, but how do we know? Has anyone proved it? No. Does the present evidence from Physics, the basic science, show that the Universe is really quite simple at base? True enough, we thought so once. But that was when we were hoping that in the end we would find, as the early Greeks scientists had believed, that all the Universe was made up of irreducible 'atoms'—which simply means ultimate objects, all simple, all quite like each other and all incapable of being reduced or broken down into anything smaller or different.

We all know that that view has been disproved—the demonstration of it that drove the argument home came when, with the Atom Bomb, the theory that matter is really not matter but a terrible form of locked-up energy, was turned into terrible fact.

Absolute certainty is no longer possible on these difficult questions as to what can happen and what has happened and what may happen. We can only take the evidence and see how far it carries us in our honest attempt to account for it all—if it is good —and not reject or suppress any of it simply because it seems to us unlikely. As a leading scientist—a physicist—recently said, the word 'incredible' went out of accurate use with Einstein—the Einsteinian Universe is quite incredible to old Common Sense.

So let us begin at where we actually are, where we find ourselves.

Granted that we cannot resist the evidence that very strange craft do range the skies and have been seen to manoeuvre by thousands of perfectly sane, informed and critically-minded witnesses. Where do they come from? (We cannot really hope to settle *what* they are, till we can track down whence they are, and where is their base. We must not overlook this one queer fact. Among all the queer facts that we have to hold in our minds while thinking on this extremely queer question, we must keep on remembering that although so many people have seen them and been fairly close to them, no one has seen one land for sure, and no one has touched one of them.

Seeing is believing, but feeling, touching, handling is knowing. Do these objects never come to rest? That would make them like the fabulous first accounts of the Bird of Paradise which was said to be so light and feathery that it could float and rest on the air; it was believed to be so buoyant that it did not need to have any feet, but with spread wings rested on the atmosphere. Surely that is so unlikely that we need not even discuss it until we have exhausted every other explanation. And there are quite a number of other explanations. (The most likely one is that before preserving the skins of the birds, the New Guinea natives cut off the wings and feet, removed the skull and body, and dried the feathered skin over a fire).

Let us then, as we should and must, start at home and work outwards, stopping immediately we can in honesty draw rein with all objections reasonably met. That means we must begin with ourselves. Not only charity begins at home, but truth and all fact-finding begins at that base, too.

We must first ask : Are these craft home-products? We have seen that most of the expert witnesses who have viewed them have not been able to get away from that base. They saw the things; they saw their astounding performance and power; but these onlookers and judges could not stretch their minds to leave the earth or even their own country. Pride of country, combining with caution against fantasy, brought these reflective people, reflecting on what they knew they had seen, to seek at home for the explanation.

That Dean of Science Editors could not think the objects were not home-products.

The same is the considered judgment of the famous case of 22nd March 1950 when Captain Adams and First Officer Anderson saw a saucer over Arkansas. They could see over twenty miles. They were at 2000 feet. They recorded the time exactly, 9.29 p.m. The disc was in view for thirty seconds. The thing had neither exhaust nor vapour trail. Till then they had mocked at these 'saucer stories'.

Now, as they declared in their statement, they just had to realise this at least was true, this was a saucer right on their tracks. And there were the other features belonging to the 'species'—the strangest, strongest blue light they had ever seen; but in this case it blinked rapidly at the topside of the saucer. The pilots blinked their landing lights, hoping it would blink back. But it was as non-committal as all these objects seem to be. Nor did any kind of head or face appear at the line of glowing ports or windows that shone along its side. Further, it showed its vast power of speed by swooping round the air-liner with consummate ease. The pilots saw the line of lit ports as the monster swept round in an amazing arc and went off—where? Yet the pilots added after reporting all that, "We know the Air Force has denied that there is anything to this Flying Saucer business; but we believe firmly that it was a secret experimental type of aircraft—not a visitor from outer space".

Well, we the public know how to make a distinction in that statement. We know that these men were so competent to recognise what their eyes showed them that they 'are right in what they affirm' but there is nothing of any evidence at all in 'what they deny'. How do they know this was a home product—why should they deny, contradict, and indeed imply that the Air Force was not speaking truthfully? This part of their statement any lawyer, any good juryman, any educated person sees at once is pure supposition tacked on to clear observation. It is natural enough; but, alas, natural behaviour is seldom if ever accurate, still less scientific.

The same kind of what we may call double-level report—of clear and open statement, and then of close and unfounded conviction—comes with the interview given by Captain Robert Adickes a T.W.A. Pilot. He, the members of his crew, and the 19 passengers aboard, all saw on the night of 28th April an object that for over five minutes flew alongside his plane. He tried to approach it but it veered away. It kept a distance of about half a mile between itself and the passenger-plane and, when Adickes turned his plane straight towards it, then it made off with that easy bound with which these craft leap away—it doubled its pace from 200 to 400 m.p.h.—and left the passenger-plane's company marvelling. Adickes owned that till then he had been a mocker of 'saucer stories'. But now what was he to do? The object was of that somewhat rare variety, the cheery red complexion; and it chose—(as some of them clearly do when they like)— to proceed on its edge, like a great wheel rolling through the sky, edge-on to the far below earth. Adickes, of course, did what all people must do who have had too great a shock to their common sense. He moved as little as he could and then clamped down even though it was on grounds that the Air Force had said could not be taken. It was a home product—it was not 'a machine from Mars'. But having made some sort of patched-up peace with his own protesting common sense, Captain Adickes added, "Whoever is building these things, I think they are dangerous flying around the air-ways. If one got out of control, it could cause an accident".

With that opinion, and with its vital importance, we can all agree. Indeed that remark is crucial and has of course occurred to everyone who has thought about this mystery. As suggested above, it gives the strongest possible support to the Authorities' statement that they are *not* responsible for such dangerous behaviour. A derelict at sea, an abandoned ship without lights drifting in the sea traffic lanes, is one of the nightmare dreads of any sea pilot or captain. But such a wild wanderer on the air traffic lanes is far more deadly. A collision at sea is very dangerous—a collision in the air at night is pure horror.

No one in his senses, no one on earth would permit such a violation of human safety. Experiment as you please and as you must. But who could ever entertain the thought, when the utmost care is taken with an occasional rocket that it shall fall in the desert, that frightfully swift craft would be permitted to charge about, unheralded, unforewarned on the ever more crowded traffic lanes of the passenger air-liners? Only by keeping these lanes clearer than any rail-tracks has it been possible to keep the casualty and crash rate so low that air-travel is a wise form of transport. Need more be said to establish the double point—that these flying objects do exist *and* their behaviour proves that they are not home products? They are handled with masterly power by someone. But that someone, though able to avoid accidents—so far—clearly does not know the stringent rules which alone make possible safe flight on our level, at our stage of developments, with the still very rudimentary and dangerous planes in which we—poor humans in our first generation of flying knowledge—go up in the air and risk our lives.

Hence we are forced back on the evidence that 'something' is up there. Perhaps there is no American whose general opinion on flying machines is more respected than that of Captain Eddie Rickenbacker; first an ace pilot himself in World War I; then a hero of some wonderful exploits in World War II, and since then one of the most enterprising promoters and organisers of civilian flying services in the whole country. Captain Rickenbacker is a man of courage, good sense, enterprise, all in the highest degree; and he is equally open-minded. He is now the active and most successful President of the big Flying Corporation, Eastern Air Lines. And he said straight out, without a moment's hesitation on 11th June—when questioned in an interview at Indianapolis—"They're real! Too many good men have seen them who don't have hallucinations".* Captain Rickenbacker knows how keen and critical is the sight and judgment of trained pilots—he has to. It is his job; and like all real masters he has gone through the job himself from the plane to his top-chair at the head of this big Company. But he added: "You can bet they belong to the United States Air Force. They're not from Mars and not from Russia."

So we see here again, as long as the expert is speaking of the fact, the actual evidence, there he is definite and authoritative. But then he leaves the positive and takes to the dangerous grounds of speculation and the dangerous side of the negative, saying what things cannot be. Of course he says: "You can bet". And, if you are the gambling sort, there is nothing you cannot bet on. But in this matter we are looking and must look for that high and convincing probability, that meeting of all objections which at last permits us to say no other conclusion is more likely, no other explanation covers the evidence so well. Granted then that we take and hold to the words of Authority, to the Air Force's statement that the discs are not their work—and we see this statement gains

* Captain Chiles and First Officer Whitted, it will be recalled are pilots of Eastern Air Lines and were flying one of this company's ships when they had their first experience. (See Chapter III).

immense practical weight from the fact that such craft charging about on the passenger traffic air-lanes present a hazard to the lives of thousands which no responsible profession (still less a Governmental authority) would ever take. What is our next step? What is the 'Whence' that we must explore?

Before leaving the territory in which most of the sightings have been made—the area of the United States, southern Canada and northern Mexico—we have to ask, however unlikely it may seem, Could these craft be coming from this district? Could they be sent up into the air—and come to roost again—from some site within this vast territory? Could they be sent up by some association that was not public but private, not governmental but independent? It is hard to think of an example to illustrate such a strange possibility. But suppose for instance that there was a body of men who thought that they could manage the world better than any one of the governments of today, men who took with desperate seriousness the popular slogan, 'One world or None' — might not such a secret society, in imitation of the old romantic secret societies such as the medieval Vehmgaricht—set itself to build such a fleet as a first step to taking over world government? The question has to be asked if we are to exhaust all possibilities.

In the past such secret societies have been very powerful and once or twice nearly decisive in world politics. Hassan, the Old Man of the Mountain, the Persian of the period of the Crusades, did with a secret organisation make his influence felt on both sides of the great struggle—between Islam and Christendom. The proposal has however only to be made to be dismissed. The North American continent, the 48 states and their environs, are now flown over day by day in every direction. Keen eyes are sweeping the ground of practically every square mile. No one has ever seen a disc rising from the ground: no one has seen a disc 'homing' on to the ground, making a landing and settling down. No—these machines have always concluded by disappearing into the farthest depth of the sky or over the vast space of the Pacific.

As we can no longer hope to track them down on the ground, flying over which they have been most often seen—the United States—we are forced to look outside. Where? Of course many people said once—far fewer do now—"Russia". Instead of singing the old popular film song, "Beyond the Blue Horizon", they now whisper "Behind the Iron Curtain". Suspicion is of course always credulous, for fear always magnifies and can never reason clearly.

If we do reason step by step, then suspicion of Russia as a source begins to wane. For this nerve-inspired, fear-provoked will-to-believe has to disregard tremendous obstacles. "Granted that the Russians have planes utterly in advance of what we have"— that is the first requirement. It is not at all probable. For it to be so, the Russians would have to possess plant ahead of that of the United States. Just to have brilliant inventors is not enough. These discs have been produced in such numbers that very big manufacturing plants must be turning them out in high quantity. When Dr. Grimm was permitted to visit Russia a year after the war to be able to answer those people who said: "We have given Russia much food: may we know how it was distributed?" he made a very interesting report. In it he said that, to those who had not seen it, the terrible thoroughness of the destruction of plant by the Germans through all the vast area of Russia which they succeeded in over-running was unbelievable. He spoke, too, of how difficult it was for Russia to repair such ingenious eradication—how, for example, in the scientific wrecking of the great Dneprostroi Power Plant the giant dynamos had been so blasted that those which could be repaired in Russia had to be sent right up to Leningrad. Nowhere near the Dneiper—which of course is a river of Russia's South—could any plant be found able to take on such a job; while a couple of the dynamos had to be sent to America for refitting. Requirement No. 1 cannot therefore be granted.

There is no reason to suspect that Russian plane output has been able to equal, far less to outpace, that of the United States. And, even if this were the case, it would only bring us to a far more abrupt and insurmountable problem. For, if the Russians had such a rich variety of immensely advanced planes, then why in the name of Historical Necessity or any other principle would they be taking the absurd risk of flying these invaluable specimens in such large numbers over the United States? Like the query "Could

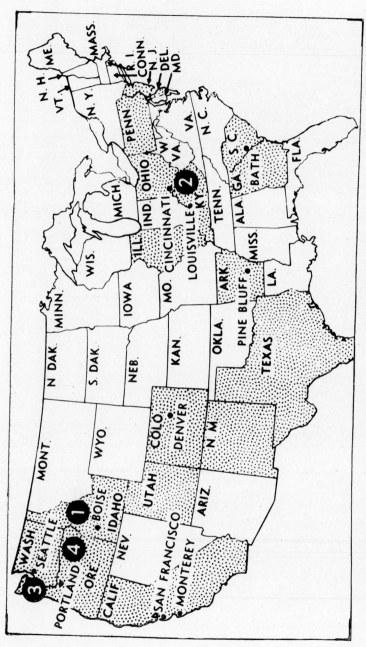

Map showing where early U.S.A. sightings occurred. Places marked with numerals indicate notable events in the 'saucer' story.

Planet News Ltd.

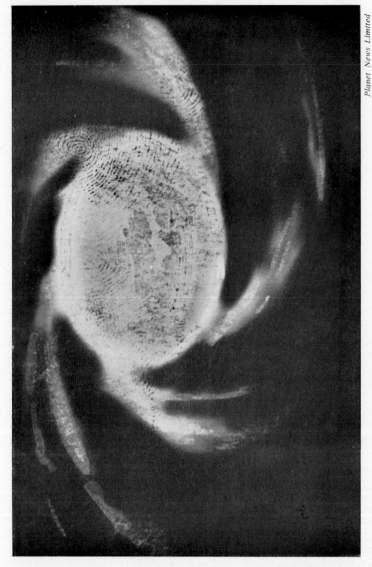

Photograph taken by Enrique Hausemann Muller, a news-reel cameraman in the Balearic Islands.

the discs be instruments of a secret society?" the question has only
to be asked to be dismissed.

If you have a secret weapon the very last thing to do is to show
it to your rival, to wave it in the sky in his face, to risk his bringing
one down, to provoke him to pursue and to hint to him how he
should invent. "Display of Might?" All that belongs to the dear
dead days of the Field of the Cloth of Gold, of flashing accoutre-
ments, silken banners, gaudy uniforms, parades and bands and
painted prows. The men who rule Russia are not sentimentalists.
Of one thing we may be sure—they never risk giving themselves
away. Just in order to impress, they would be, perhaps of all the
rulers of the world, least inclined to do this, or to hint at what
cards they actually hold. They may agree with those outside
their Iron Curtain on very few points; but on one they certainly do
concur, the old adage:—

> " 'A shut mouth and a poker face' wins the game. 'A stuck-out
> tongue and a grinning grimace', will lose it."

Besides, the discs have been seen all over the world. Take for
example the set that Commander Orrego, the Chilean Naval Officer
saw whirling above his Antarctic Base, and photographed. What
in the name of Economic Necessity and the Inevitable Revolution
would Russian planes be doing down there waltzing in the long,
long, Polar day? There are no wage-slaves in sweated factories
in Antarctica to look up and be heartened by the promise of deliv-
erance waving in the sky; there are no serfs of the soil toiling to
raise crops for landlords and longing to own the fruitful earth and
needing, as the Bishop Herber's hymn says, to be delivered "from
error's chain". You do not waste fuel and time, risk losing invaluable machines, gamble with losing even more precious secrets,
either by rushing over a rival's country or spinning above the most
desolate parts of the earth. Still less do you do so when those
desolate parts are areas you do not control. For then your fallen
gear can be recovered by others who will discover the source of
your secret supremacy.

But if it is not the Russians, then who? It must be someone!
Yes, that second part of the statement stands. It is true, if anything is true. For these discs are driven by intelligence, high

E

intelligence, the highest we have come across so far. Could they be British? Great Britain certainly, all the world allows, is in the very first rank of progressive design with jet planes. But would the British Government fly its newest type all over the United States and on the traffic air-lanes of that country? Of course not. Would Britain, any more than Russia, send these precious things to waltz in the welkin over the South Pole? Again, who can fail to say "No".

Britain and the United States are now closer together than since 1774, and even earlier than that. The United Nations is a more serious manifestation of world unity than has ever appeared before for mankind. It is impossible to think that Britain would trespass over the territory of a friendly nation and in doing so risk the lives of the nationals of that country as well as the loss of the trespassing ship.

Could any other country, any of the remaining 'Powers'—as they used to be called—be thought to be competent to put on such a show? Some people have said, 'Spain might!'*

But could any designer make such a number and such a variety of craft in a country not industrialised? Spain has always been a backward country. She imported most of the weapons to fight her intensely destructive civil war. Could Spain today, with the help of a few refugee Nazi brains, sow the upper air round the globe, and in flights over the United States, with super-original aircraft? Spain, which never produced one super-successful car to compete on the pre-war world automobile market? We have only to write out the question to see that it is answered. Spain could not.

---

* On 14 May 1949 this view was being publicised by *The Washington Daily News*. This paper held that not only were the discs at last beyond dispute as a fact but that they were not Russian, that expert opinion was convinced that they could not be so, and also, in structure, they were a new 'gyroscopic' design. Walter Winchell, the famous news-commentator, in his syndicated column, allowed the gyroscopes but denied the geography. He had already gone over to the flying saucers as a fact and not an illusion. With rightful triumph therefore he quoted on June 5th that *The New York World Telegram* had, after some weeks, confirmed his judgment. For this paper maintained that the Air Force had just secured a picture of three discs . They had appeared flying together over the Newfoundland transatlantic air-base of Stevensville, and when chased had easily outdistanced their fastest pursuers.

Italy or France? These two at least did produce much fine and pioneering automobile work and some interesting planes. They had and have some plant—though the Italian equipment was terribly damaged and the French has not been able to keep at all near to the American spurt of production, even considering the different scales of the two countries. No: all the bigger countries of Europe are out, now that Germany is still in two pieces, if not three.

Asia—outside Russian Asia? Outside the Iron Curtain we know that Asia still waits to be industrialised even to our present pitch of motor manufacture. The same is true of South America. Japan is under complete surveillance. There remain South Africa, Australia and New Zealand. And to them what was said of Britain applies, with the further demurrer—none of them is industrialised to the pitch of Britain.

We have gone around the world. Forced from finding any perch for these flyers in the country over which they have most flown, we have traversed the globe. We have found witnesses of their flights all over our sphere but nowhere have we found any place from which we can with any real possibility say that they rise and to which they return.

We can find no 'Whence' for them anywhere on the whole earth's surface. Let us be certain of that, for that certainty is a very grave finding. We should not, we could not give up the search to find for them some foothold, some resting spot, some production centre. There are no secret places now upon our earth. Our eyes have now scanned—and in a few hours from any centre can rush up and out and scan—any spot on the surface of our planet. No wonder that, faced with that fact, we try to avoid the evidence that flying objects (which have no place to 'home' back to) do ride the skies. No wonder that, when the evidence forces us to own that such sky-riders are up aloft, we fall back feebly on what has been denied —that we say, we *must* have made them, though we do not know that we did!

At this point of the story we must pull ourselves together. We must recall that we are dealing with evidence and its interpretation —two different, though always closely combined, things. We must recall that all we have to guide us in finding out anything in this world is probability. Sometimes it is so high that we can say that, in anything that matters, we are certain. Sometimes one's opinion has to wait, putting the data in a suspense account.

Of course it could be possible that some out-of-the-way tribe had made these things—but it is so wildly improbable that we can safely dismiss any such theory. It may be possible that some home-production plant has made and is making them for we must remember that, except for some propositions of logic, and even of that the logicians now do not seem to be as sure as they were, anything is *possible*. The Universe has never given us a set of rules and said it will never break them, or given us a guarantee that it will never produce anything but what is on the list. But it does seem clear that probability now forces us to seek for any other possible place where these ceiling-cruisers could come from. Not till we have searched really everywhere have we the right to say, "I have absolutely no idea" or "I don't believe one word I'm told". Neither the denial that we make them nor the declaration that they exist, that they have been seen, really lets us rest.

But if there is no place for them to 'home' on the whole earth, then, in the name of Noah's Dove, where can they find an ark where they can return to roost? They cannot spend all the time circling above . . . Or can they . . . ? Well, till we can track them down or up—we must find any further clue from what we can discover from their performance. An arrow tells you something, if not much, about a bow; and a bullet, to a ballistics and gunnery specialist, says something about the type of gun that fired it and the kind of force that drove it, and the distance it may have travelled. So that before posing any more "Whence" queries, we must go carefully over our ancillary evidence. "From the foot you can deduce the stature of Hercules", said the Greek sculptors: and there was an older saying, "From one claw you can construct or imagine the lion".

From our study of the craft we may come to be able to suspect the type of port and even the ship-yard base from which these super-argosies have sailed.

Chapter IX

THE CRAFT AND THEIR POWER

THE first thing for us to get clear in our minds is the range of craft with which we have been presented. Indeed the name Saucer or Disc may soon cease to be suitable as a general or generic name for this kind of air visitor. It does describe the all-over appearance of a common type—as you may say that most things that swim in the sea are fishes, but you have to add that there are things swimming in the sea utterly unlike fishes—e.g. the octopus. So in the upper levels of that air-sea—the atmosphere—on the floor of which we crawl—we are now gazing up at the hulls of cruisers of very different patterns.

As a start however let us take that species we call the Disc or Saucer. It certainly has a number of varieties. Let us start with the first to be sighted since the outbreak of sightings in June 1947, the famous sightings made by Arnold of Boise, Idaho, while in his plane. He judged, by gauging them against the mountain peaks —along the ridges of which they were flying—that they were twenty miles or more away and then (as he could compare them with a large plane, a DC-4, that was flying in the same circuit of his vision) he estimated that the discs must be somewhat smaller than that plane. From his second sighting—at 7 a.m. on 30th July, when he was flying over Oregon—he saw several small discs—he judged these to be not more than two to three feet across and light brown in tint.

The famous sightings, made under perfect conditions at White Sands Testing Grounds in New Mexico in April, May and June 1949, confirmed that these two types do exist. There is a type which is about 100 feet across and with it was seen also a far smaller type. On the June observing, the two small discs that examined the up-rushing rocket and then made such an amazing acceleration when they outpaced the rocket and shot into the

69

depth of the sky, were, according to the theodolite readings, not more than 20 inches in diameter. The one sighted in May seems to have been the same size as that sighted in April—just over 100 feet across. There may be one a little smaller than this. For the other theodolite observation—that by the surveying team at Emmet, Idaho, on 20th February 1948, showed a craft about the size of a small plane (Piper Cub plane).*

Then there are varieties of the shape. Some seem to be discs, saucers, plates, or flat circular objects. Others seem to have a bite out of the side which appears to be their stern. The thing that flew over Phoenix, Arizona, seemed to have such a bite in it. But the bite-effect may be given by streaks of fume coming like widespread twin tail-plumes. The Emmet disc had only a kind of foam gathering at its stern as it flew, and the observers thought the stern-indentation was the sharply incurved aperture given in the conventional pattern of the human heart. The thing was flying with the point or "base" of the heart directed forward—like a rather blunt arrowhead.

It is notoriously difficult to judge of the size or even the shape of objects high in the sky, especially when they are moving rapidly, unless you can range an instrument on them. But we see in those cases where the observations were made without instruments that they were afterwards confirmed substantially by those who were so equipped, and trained to use such appliances.

We must add another important sighting, not mentioned in this summary so far, but to be noted again when we return to the problem of "Whence?" At Flagstaff, Arizona, where the climate is so good and the atmosphere so clear that the Harvard Observatory was placed there by Lowell, the famous astronomer, after whom the Observatory is named, Dr. Seymour L. Hess, the resident astronomer on 22nd May 1950 reported to *The Arizona Daily Sun* that, while studying weather conditions, he had seen a bright object, a disc visible to the naked eye. He then trained binoculars on it. This convinced him that it was not a plane of

* *The Denver Post* of April 9th 1950 printed a letter from an observer who had seen a disc in the Los Angeles district and who described it as 'heart-shaped'. 'It did not spin but moved with the point of the heart headed forward'.

any known type, and he was made sure of two other things. The machine was cutting through the clouds, and could not therefore be a weather balloon, for that would drift with the wind. Further, "four-power binoculars" showed that the object was from three to six feet in diameter. The time was 12.15 p.m.

Then we come to two mass-observations. Crowds saw the object and watched it for some time. These two cases are perhaps the most important of all the sightings so far made. The first is that which ended with the death of Captain Mantell. There, as the reader will remember, the object was sighted first by State Police as it came up the sky over Kentucky. The State Police alerted the Military Police. The machine was travelling in the direction of the Godman Flying field. But while it was still nearly 100 miles away, many people in the town of Madisonville had caught sight of it. Still the really important fact about these findings is that they were made simultaneously by so many people *so widely scattered*. More than 150 miles apart, people looking up saw the same thing, the same odd object in the sky. What does that mean? It means—a very simple form of triangulation will show—that the object must have been at a vast height. And if it were so high, it must have been of great size to have been visible to the human eye. In fact there seems little chance of escaping the conclusion that this was the largest air-ship ever seen, save perhaps one more case to be mentioned in a moment.*

This was a very mother of discs and perhaps that poetic phrase may get quite near being an exact description—perhaps it was the mother ship in which the smaller craft—like dinghys hauled on

---

* There is also a *third* sighting of a 'monster' given in one of the 'releases' of 'Project Saucer'. But this report lacks clear detail. We are told that an unnamed man holding a private licence saw a vast object flying towards him. He first thought it was a normal plane but saw when it came closer that it was perfectly round and flat and that it emitted no sound. He gave its size as of the bulk of six human planes each of the size of the large plane called a B.29. Its speed was three times that of a jet plane. All that such a report establishes is that someone who may be a good observer saw something that was very large, pretty certainly a disc and that it was going faster than any plane he had ever seen before. It was sighted over the State of Oklahoma.

board a schooner—could take refuge after their exploratory flights, as Noah's dove came back to rest in the Ark. It may have been anything between 700 or perhaps 1,000 feet across. Such a thing needs considerable evidential support, even when we have allowed that discs 100 and more feet across do ride the skies.

On 22nd of March—this is the second case— a perfect observation of this or a sister monster was made. Idyllwild is a charming resort on the slopes that rise to Mount Jacinto—the 10,000 foot mountain that in California stands sentinel between the inner desert and the outer coastal belt, a couple of hours run S.S.E. of Los Angeles. Visibility there is generally good. The little town stands high, the air has a desert clarity. Visitors are numerous. A number were watching the sky, because two jet planes were practising high up. The performance of these craft is still so novel to all interested in aviation that when they are lunging through the sky most people will pause to see how these 'man-manned super-bullets' are making and mending their pace.

Of course very little can be published about them: they are so near—if not right upon—the growing edge of our speed ambitions. There, as far as the public knows, lies the real armament race. The sky, the upper sky, is now the world track for the greatest Marathon ever run—a race in which we may in the end run so fast that we shall run ourselves out—run ourselves off the planet's surface into what unfathomable night?

In the crowd of perhaps 100 people were two who were peculiarly qualified to take an expert professional interest.

They were Air Force sergeants. And they both had had a peculiarly appropriate training in keen observation—even for Air Force men. Bill Elder, aged 25, had served in the Navy in the last war. He had time and again acted as look-out man when at the last the desperate Japanese tried to hold back the closing grapple of the American sea-and-air forces on the home islands by sending up the famous Kamikaze or 'suicide pilots' to swoop down out of the sun and fatally crash themselves, blowing up on the decks of battleships in the hope of exploding them. Elder, therefore, was alert, with good vision and trained judgment. His companion,

Bob O'Hara, who is four years younger, had an equally intense training. He had been 'spotter' for the Air Force in air-sea rescue work—scanning the blurred or dazzling surface of the ocean for the tiny dark spot which is the head of a man, perhaps at that moment sinking. These two were watching the jets through field-glasses—modern field-glasses that cut out glare and give almost perfect visibility.

Such were the circumstances in which the two trained watchers and the rest of the crowd saw, riding the upper air, a huge disc. The two 'spotters' thought it might be at least 40,000 feet up. They noted that it could have been no balloon, however tremendous—balloons cannot go against the wind. That this one was going against the high wind was shown by the drift of the vapour trails of the jet-planes: and it was far too big for a weather balloon. Further, it showed that queer complexion which the large discs have so often been found to display. It had the silver sheen of metal, but the underside showed that warm rosy tint noted in a number of other cases.

That the object must have been at a tremendous height was proved by the long period for which it remained in sight: it was said to have been observed altogether for some four hours. People not at Idyllwild saw it. In one place a tripod telescope was ranged at it. Of course it may have been far higher up than 40,000 feet. Probably it was riding at those extreme levels where air thins out for good, those super-levels at which the White Sands observers were able definitely to calculate that their visitors were able to ride.

The two trained watchers at Idyllwild, however, were certain of two things—one that it was a craft they had never heard of, still less seen (they added a caveat that they were not to be thought to imagine that it might have come from outside the earth). The other point does add a grain of knowledge to our scanty information. The watchers were quite sure that the thing resembled a big, thick pan-cake. That, of course, is the discs' standard figure. But what is not standard is that this one seemed to have a hind fin sticking out of it.

The description sounds like that of a sun-fish on its side. The

73

observers thought that this great fin 'whirled'. Could that 'fin' have been the fume or smoke which the monster that rushed across Kentucky showed? It certainly could not have been a paddle or an oar of any sort. One thing is clear—these super-ships do not need any sort of blade to push them along. They are as much beyond the jets as the jets have gone beyond the old propeller type of aircraft.

Then there is, at the very end of May (the 30th) Captain William Sperry's* account of another craft which may not fit into any of the above categories. He told the National Air Port at Washington, D.C., that, at 7,500 feet, seven miles west of Mount Vernon, in the state of Virginia he found that his craft (one of the big DC-6s) which he was flying with passengers for American Airlines was having—literally—circles run round it by—? He called it "a submarine with lights".

We'll get back to that in a minute. What we can note at once, for it is without doubt, is that he said this thing actually circled his plane twice. His pace was about 300 miles per hour. So this giant 'cigar', if one may so term it, shows, mechanically, tremendous speed and masterly maneouvreability. You do not go looping and re-looping in front of the prow of a plane going at 300 miles per hour unless, in the Irish horse-racing phrase, "you have the legs of her". And, as its mechanical prowess shows what was the machine's capacity, its actual performance tells us something of the psychology of its rider, its pilot. He certainly was inquisitive, showing more curiosity perhaps than in any other of these cases.

* Captain Sperry has now written a full letter to *Flying*, a technical periodical on aviation largely for experts. He not only says that he would maintain that the speed of the object was far beyond the limits of any known aircraft and indeed 'fantastic', but he adds that the shape was clear to him and his two assistants, for the object as they watched passed (in its circling of their plane) across the face of the full moon. The particular and important addition that he makes to his account and to our knowledge of the various 'spaceship' types, was that there was a very brilliant fluorescent bluish light on the forward end of the object. In his sketch Captain Sperry shows that the light came from the very tip of the 'disc'.

The Editors of *Flying* say, at the end of the correspondence column, that they believe, and they are supported by 'top-notch Washington military correspondents', that no public commentator has satisfactorily explained the saucers.

This was the clearest proof up to date that whoever is looking in, is wondering about us and trying, with a careful combination of caution and curiosity, to find out what we can do and how we behave.

As to what the actual shape of the thing was, surely we can say it was probably not a disc. It was far more likely to have been one of the long tube type with their rows of lights and that weirdly-lit fore-cabin. For that is the second clearly defined type. Then there may be a huge glow—but that again may only be a disc—and these discs are evidently objects that swell from a rim to considerable thickness at their centre. Thus a bulky disc might be taken for a globe.

Finally, to finish with their cut and contour, there are the best photographs so far, those taken by Paul Trent in Oregon. These have been reproduced first in *The McMinville Telephone Register*, the paper of the town outside which Mr. Trent has his farm. Then they reached the foremost illustrated weekly, the New York paper, *Life*. Now they have been printed by the London *Sunday Dispatch*. They show a disc, but with a small central 'mast'. We need to add this further point so as to be able to go on, with all the information we have, to the next section, 'The Craft's Power'. This saucer, like the rest, cruised noiselessly and left no vapour trail.

We need all the information we can get to help us on this second point of our enquiry about these craft. Of their shape we have some idea. Of their pace or paces, of their range or ranges of speed, we have some further notion—though here again, when almost any pace seems possible, from a quiet brooding to a speed of 18,000 miles per hour, we are almost left without power of proper speculation, because we are so embarrassed by the wealth of possibilities. The power of acceleration is, too, so far outside the terms in which we think of possible travel, that our minds can hardly order the findings of our senses.

We must be very patient. For no wonder people who are brought up on text-books feel that anything that breaks the rules of deportment laid down for objects (by those who thought they knew what all objects must do) just cannot be.

The power problem provides the next big step our minds have to take. More than the craft, this question of their speed seems to rule out any human designer. How are they driven? To start with the simpler problem, it would seem that some are not driven of themselves. They may be remote-controlled. That idea with our human craft is already getting settled in our minds. But we must remember how odd it is —the idea that objects which seem to be directed by someone inside them, which show a human way of avoiding obstacles and seeking out that object and target, are really being directed by someone far away by intangible 'fibres' of control, in other words by rays or radio.

Was there any plane bearing the 'light' that Gorman chased above the flying field at Fargo? Perhaps a transparent 'lantern' did carry that intelligent will-of-the-wisp. But it certainly behaved with a freedom, dash and rush that would suggest that so small and maybe so tenuous a thing was not itself 'manned'. It was being bobbed and whisked in front of the flyer's nose as an angler high up on the bank, and standing in another element (air), whisks and bobs his bait in front of a submerged fish. In this case, however we must remember the 'remote control', the putative 'angler', did show a consideration for the 'fish' that we seldom display. But, as we shall see in the next chapter, when we try to penetrate the mystery still farther and to discuss 'Crews and Views', it is not permissible for us to say: "The craft was so small, the speed so great, the twists and lunges and kicks so deadly violent to anyone inside, that of course it could not have been 'manned'—no intelligent creature could go through such a milling and live; let alone whether any such creature could, in the first place, get inside a craft a couple of feet across!"

No, our minds may have to be stretched still farther; and meanwhile, in preparation for that painful process, let us try to keep them as open as we can. We must not shut down. If we do, we may have our minds wrenched open too violently for their peace and maybe for their balance.

So turn again to the problem of powering a plane to remain poised *and* to go at 18,000 miles per hour; of powering a plane to fly at more than 50 miles high: of powering a plane perhaps over

1,000 feet across, which evidently never comes to earth and rushes round the globe as if it were a tiny satellite, and takes refuge when tired (either tired in itself or weary of us), not down on the earth, but up in the sky.

Have these machines ever been seen in trouble? Are they flawlessly efficient? The Maury Island Mystery opened with a disc which seemed to need some sort of doctoring. But for that report we have to trust a witness who apparently was far from willing to talk to the enquirer who passed the story on. Efforts to confirm or get the story repeated were in vain. So we cannot say for sure that for some time anyone saw, in anything which could be called trouble, a disc or a tube or a giant globe, or even one of the 'small golden globes' that were now and then reported as bobbing about near places in flight. Then came 'a lone observer' from the woods of the Northwest saying he thought that one had dropped into a lake or at least dropped something into a lake. This, again, is vagueness itself. Granted that the disc was there, granted that it dropped something, it might be a matter of furnace-cleaning.

What seems more important is a United Press report from Seattle, Washington, on 29th April 1950.

Thirty employees of one of the city light sub-stations all declared that they saw a double-decked balloon moving majestically, through the sky. While they watched, as it was sailing over South Seattle, it exploded. They informed the police. The eye-witnesses indicated the area where they were sure they had seen fragments of the "ship" coming down, settling toward the earth. An area of some sixteen city-blocks was indicated. The police, with firemen to aid them, searched the whole of this area. Not a vestige of anything odd, nor of anything which could have been exploded, was to be found.

What is one to make of such a report? Do these creatures of the upper air, when they feel their end is near, break up and then dissolve so that by the time their fragments have reached terra firma they have volatilised into invisible gas—"and, like this insubstantial pageant faded, leave not a rack behind"?*

---

* There is a possible confirmation of this in the report from Copenhagen on 18th February where a farmer reported that two discs came over his house. One went on, while the other alighted and 'in less than a minute disintegrated into thousands of flowing sparks.'

All we can say at this point, and when we are considering the power of these objects, is that any evidence that even they on occasion falter and fail, is almost the weakest part of the whole witnessed story.

But we have a possible clue—just possible—that they do get together now and then, and that this getting together may be to pep each other up, to do some kind of recharging exercise. The first case comes from Idaho again—Idaho, that rather out-of-the-way State once famous because of the religious conservatism of its inhabitants, so that the whole area was alliteratively called the Bible Belt—the kind of place where farmers farm for six days and fundamentalize on the seventh. Idaho may however add the discs to its 'Belt' for certainly it has taken a leading part in observing this kind of phenomenon.

Remember that case at Twin Falls—that was in Idaho. There the disc was sighted by a couple of observers who thought it was sky-blue and fairly low down. Further, though it did not seem as low down as all that, the tree-tops were, when it raced over them, in what A. E. Housman calls "in trouble", like the wood on Wenlock Edge.

Now that very same day at a place called Salmon Dam, again in Idaho, two miners were made to look up to the sky. They were not sky-gazing, admiring the clear air—miners, one supposes, generally have an earthward look. But they had good hearing. And what they heard set them looking about. The sound was a strange and loud—an unfamiliar roar. It was coming from the sky. Then they caught a glimpse of a flashing object in the sky. They both were clear about it. Two discs, so bright that they reminded the upgazing miners of shining mirrors, were waltzing away in what seemed an excess of speed and energy.

Let us not comment yet until we have repeated again the description of the Chilean Commander Orrego, stationed in Antarctica and gazing aloft into the lit 'white night' of the South Polar summer—"We saw flying saucers, one above the other, turning at tremendous speeds". For fun? Out of the wild joy of living, having a day off from weary work of cataloguing our dreary cities and trying to make sense of our sooty web of things? Or had they a reason for so behaving, had they a need so to behave?

Glance back through the findings as to the signs of energy given by the betraying trails and smears and vapour-wakes and sky smudges. We do know that the huge thing over Tucson, Arizona, did puff and pant in the true old-fashioned combustion-engine way. A long stream of fine smoke (as when the combustion is high and the furnaces are clean) and then a puff of denser smoke when the machine was brought to a pause, as the master of this giant craft considered Tucson from the sky? And the even huger thing that raced across Kentucky, that, too, was said to have glowed fearsomely from its stern. Perhaps the huge 'paddle' seen by the Idyllwild observers and the two Air Sergeants suggested that it was some kind of hind-plume of smoke. But the first theodolite observation—again an Idaho prize, the one seen at Emmet—that showed only a little foam round the stern, like the lather on a chin about to be shaved. And most discs have shown nothing.

The tubes do show a good, fine, kicking and splashing flame. In such cases we may say that we are—as far as theory is concerned —if not on the level, (or well within our depth) at least not hopelessly out of it. This is jet propulsion ahead of ours, but evidently along the same path—maybe even the frothing heart-shape disc seen by one of the first theodolites to settle its eye on a disc, even that may have been a fine form of some super-efficient fuel. But the silent flitting of nearly all of them gets far more mysterious when to it we add the lack of any visible exhaust, any smoke.

So now back to the dance. The dance that was seen to take place with a couple of discs over Salmon Dam, Idaho, came on the very day on which at Twin Falls, in the same State, a single disc had been seen comparatively low down. Now was that disc in trouble, as it made the trees twist and writhe as it passed over? Was its colour, which had sunk to a blue from the usual flashing white, a sign of depletion, a magnetic anaemia of its system? And when the two were seen together, flashing like mirrors, surely that was brighter than they are usually described. They are said to "flash white", but this blaze as of a mirror in the sun, that is above the usual 'albedo', as astronomers call the brightness-quality of the stars they study.

Shall we for the moment assume that the two had just raised their temperature, made their strange circulation brisk and equal to scaling the sky, by having a whirl round each other? Whirl two objects, each of which is a 'coil' properly 'wound', and what happens? It is as familiar as, at base, it is mysterious—electricity is generated. Are these discs so recharging each other? Right down at the South Pole were they caught at the same game — where perhaps they thought no one would be on the look-out (the case at Salmon Dam may have been an emergency 'transfusion' or artificial respiratory exercises).*

There might be another reason for going off to the South Pole. Long ago Dr. Gilbert, the able physician to that odd old invalid, Queen Elizabeth, and also, on the side, one of the fathers of Electrical Science, made the amazingly penetrating remark, considering the state of knowledge of his time, "The Earth itself is a Giant Magnet".†

Now to-day the struggle to find out what the relation may be between electricity and Magnetism has reached a new crisis. Einstein, as we all know, thinks he is on the verge of getting, indeed may already have, the formula which will settle that. When we remember what came in so few years, from Einstein's first big break-through in the world of ideas—the notion that matter and energy are really two aspects of the same thing—we must feel a certain awe when we think what will come of the marriage which we are trying to arrange in our minds between electricity and magnetism. But if it is the next step, and if it leads to power (as all knowledge seems to do so, since the vast mind of Francis Bacon drove that utilitarian obsession into our heads), well then, people who are so far ahead—and on the same line as we, as far as travel is concerned—such a people with such craft as we have to admit

* Compare this with Fred Johnson's account (see Chapter II) of how, while he watched the half dozen discs up above him in the Cascades, his compass-needles whirled.

† Later on we will see that lately we have discovered that Mars, too, is a magnet.

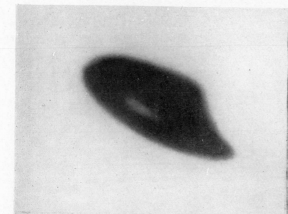

This flying object was twice snapped at dusk Monday as it circled north of Phoenix. William A. Rhodes, 4333 North 14th street, first shot the picture at the left as the slow-flying object was approaching him. As it banked to make a tight turn, he obtained the picture above, showing clearly the shape of the object. In seconds, Rhodes said, the "disc" shot away to the west at high speed. It had made three whirling turns north of the city, after approaching from the west. Aircraft identification experts yesterday would not hazzard opinions on the object's nature.

Speedy 'Saucer' Zips Through Local Sky

By ROBERT C. HANIKA

THE FIRST clearly recorded photographs of what is believed to be a mysterious "flying disc" which has 33 states in America and even a few foreign countries on edge with its peculiar activities, was taken by an amateur Phoenix photographer.

Reproduced in the Arizona Republic today, the photographs were made by William A. Rhodes, 4333 North 14th street, who was on his way to his workshop in the rear of his home when he heard the distinctive "whoosh" of what he believed to be a P-80 or Shooting Star jet-propelled plane.

Rhodes snatched a camera from his workshop bench and by the time he reached a small mound at the rear of his home, the object had circled his home once and was banking in tight circles to the south at an altitude of approximately 1,000 feet, he said.

IN THE overcast sky the object continued its speedy flight from north to south and directly east of his stance. Rhodes snapped the hurtling missile by sighting along-

(Exclusive Republic

WINDOW ROCK,
velopment of the hu;
helium gas located
Corners area of the N
reservation as a poten
income for the Nava;
discussed today at the
sions of the Navajo '
cil here today.

Norman Littell, W;
C., attorney, urged eff
about the execution o
vantageous contract v
eral government for th
gas for government u

Littell, who came
request of Sam Ahk
tribal council chairm
cently visited Washing
ed belief that terms o
contract are not favor
to the Navajo nation

HE SAID IT is e
Four Corners heliun
tains 788,000,000 cubic
comparatively rare ele

Littell declared, h
he was certain the N
would want "Uncle S;
first priority to pi
helium for use in mil
tions and for national
poses.

Helium, a nonexplos
inflammable gas is
military forces in lig
craft. Because it is
air it also is being us
airplane tires.

The Four Corners
discovered six years
course of oil drilling c
that area. During the
line was built to G
which point it was sh
tainers to all military
at home and overseas
er-than-air craft were

THERE ARE only a
helium in the United S
Chairman Ahkeah
council meeting with
his recent visit to W
discuss Navajo need
bers of congress and
ernment official:
"What we need no
is schooling and ho
need better schools, a

William A. Rhodes, Phoenix, Arizona

A cutting from *The Arizona Republic* 9th July 1947 showing William Rhode's photograph referred to on page 13.

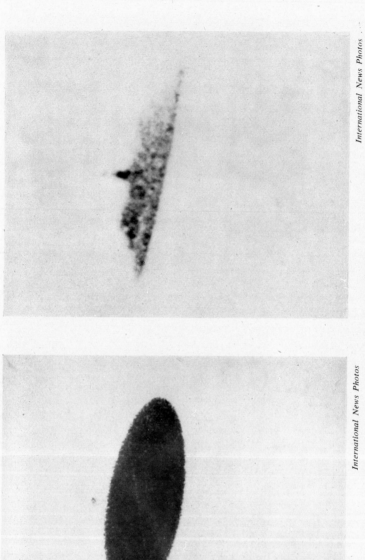

Detailed pictures from photographs taken by Paul Trent at McMinville, Oregon, referred to on page 75.

they possess, such a people would power those craft, would they not, with some form of super-energy?

One of the things, indeed the basic thing that makes flight so hard and kept us down on earth so long, was and is just this mysterious but ever present drag, gravity. Now, suppose that magnetism is, as it were, the other pole of gravity? Every force seems to have its complement in this middle cosmos of balance and of action and reaction. The magnet is there before our eyes every day, and we know that negative and positive electricity seem to be the very basis of everything that gives us the sense of touch, everything we can see and handle. Can it be that these discs (and other super sky-craft) with their super-performance, with not only their appalling speed of 18,000 miles per hour, but with their ability to demonstrate that dream of all air-plane designers, a craft that will hover silently as long as it wishes in the air at any height, can it be that they have the power that such a performance seems to demand, the power to resist gravity with its counter-force, a negative reaction to the pull of the earth, as on the negative pole of the magnet objects are not drawn in but driven out.

At any big show of electrical experimental gadgets, it has been for years a standard petty 'conceit' to show an object of weight yet raised and held in what seems empty air—because a suitably arranged magnet is holding it up. This toy perhaps the disc masters have now mastered. And maybe they go to the South Pole, because, down there, at that end of the world-magnet, they can recharge themselves best? Theory of course, but theory in an attempt to make the actual observed facts at all possible; as doctors say of patients who cannot keep food in their stomachs, to make it possible to retain what observation is ramming down our unwilling throats.

Of course such masters of the magnetic disc would be ahead of us. If they have that sort of plane and that sort of power, then we cannot escape this conclusion:— They are so far ahead of us that we may begin to see why it was impossible to find their homing site in any of the countries of the world.

Now that we have considered the Craft and their Power, what are we to do? Have we any other possible guide to help us, so

F

we may return to the 'Whence?' problem? Or must we throw in our hand and say, "Spontaneous, cataclysmic generation, if you like —that, of some forgotten spell of Merlin, which someone has found and is muttering to himself!" Let us, before we cry, "Anything may happen anywhere, so why try to order or argue anything?" let us try to see, if now we have two suggestions to make about the discs and their companions, whether they may have a mother-ship or ships high aloft and whether they may be able to resist gravity when they are low down and even stationary, and thus not acting as satellites of the earth, getting a free ride on the outer rim of our rotation. From these two possibilities about Craft and Power we may make some deductions as to the Crews and their Views.

Chapter X
THE CREWS AND THEIR VIEWS

WE shall have to start at the wrong end, if the right end is to find the creature and then study its behaviour. We cannot expose whoever—if anyone—is inside the disc, the tube, or the globe. He certainly is safely encapsuled in his husk or shell, and perhaps has to be. Certainly when you are going at 18,000 miles per hour you have to be shut up pretty securely if you are made of anything that we call a body, a living body. So we shall try to find out their views by watching their muffled if magically swift behaviour. And to find out their views we shall be on safest ground—where all seems terribly up in the air—if we try to gather what it is that they seem to view.

"Show me your tastes and I will tell you your character" is an old and obvious motto. What are they interested in? For our interests do, as it were, cast a shadow on our minds. We have been watching them only a couple of years; but already it may be that their interests have shifted a bit. Or perhaps we have—it would be the better way to put it—made them shift, jolted them out of a rut, made them brisker.

When birds have not been disturbed by man, they are far more unwary and casual than when once *we* have been about, to cause them to keep out of the way, or at least to observe their proper distance. When the discs were first seen some of the most interested sighting seemed to suggest that they—or their directors—might be in a contemplative frame of mind. They brooded quite a bit, hung above and gazed down.

A good example of this was a report of an event during the last week of July 1948. The first story, handled by the United Press and afterwards carefully vouched for, came from the peaceful and somewhat out-of-the-way town of Alice, Texas. Five reputable citizens saw the incident. That is enough, but nothing big. What

was big and strange was the time, the time the object under observation stayed on view. It seemed simply to have anchored itself
aloft. For nearly two days it remained stationary.

Spherical, and giving off very little light, it appeared to the
observers to be some 5,000 feet up in the air. Eventually planes
were sent over to investigate. But then, perhaps not unnaturally,
the patient 'watcher of the skies' gave up its vigil.

We may ask why did he wait so long? And we may add another
question, more pointed. Would he now be left to ride quietly on
the sky? The answer to that latter question is, of course, No. As
to the first question of his lengthy brood, can we ask ourselves
what it is that these visitors want to find out? Obviously they are
seeking information—there is no sign that they are planning
invasion. They have let much of the advantage of their position
slip away—the element of surprise was permitted to evaporate two
years ago. Let us then deduce what we can from their machines,
and then, from that, try to construe their manoeuvres.

Are they at all like us? Yes, they are in some wonderfully
reassuring ways. Maybe, after all, it is good that we cannot see
them, for we can the better judge them (in the interval) by their
acts. For their acts are those of—one says it advisedly — very
circumspect, very intelligent gentlemen. There is everything to
support such a reassuring verdict and nothing to tell against it. Of
their intelligence, that it is day-bright, of the highest standard, of
the most penetrating insight and understanding, it is hard to doubt.
All that we long and strain to do in the very height of mechanical
and dynamical research seems in their hands. But to this is added
a considerateness that seems equal to their power. We have to start
the last sentence with 'But', when we ought naturally to begin it
with 'And'. For in the squalid world in which we squirm, (hiding
our heads in the sand, filled with panic fear at our fellows' possible
triumphs in "winning power over the environment"), we cannot
think of power as anything but added perils, a fresh temptation to
mutual slaughter. So we have to say "But" instead of "And". As
though compassion, patience and the wish to understand were the
opposites of, and in eternal conflict with the capacity to do what we
want, and to control circumstances to fulfil our aims! Except for

the sad accident in the Mantell affair (and then the great ship was in headlong flight from its midget pursuer) these visitors have always not only tried to give right of way and get off anyone else's tracks but have succeeded. They have behaved with a deportment which shows not merely *savoir-faire* but real considerateness. Let us then, when trying to track the paths of their enquiries, see a little way by asking ourselves what we should do if we possessed power that made us considerate and proud, wise and not paranoiac?

Well, if we came upon a people much behind ourselves we would behave—as, thank Heaven (since anthropology has come in) we have done in some cases on our meeting another culture. We would conduct ourselves with patience and courtesy and wait for those into whose presence we had come to allow us to advance. Meanwhile we should be quietly observant, and see how much our eyes could teach us about the character of our involuntary hosts.

If then these visitors had—and had to have—their first views of us from a very considerable distance, what would be their first conclusion? We know that the first photograph that has been secured from a film sent up in a rocket that reached 100 miles high showed a great stretch of the Southwest of the United States. You could recognise the Gulf of California into which the Colorado River flows. But of course no hint appears on that, the first true and actual large scale map, no suggestion that this vast stretch of land has any occupants. With the best magnification and the clearest lens our proud cities would perhaps show an ambiguous stain on the landscape—not as striking as a spot of a "mosaic virus" infection that mottles the surface of a leaf. We ourselves, "the measure of all things", "the crown of creation"—as we have with modest self-awareness named our presence—we should be far less prominent than lice.

As then any visitor from far up aloft came careening down, he would first see our stain-towns. And then, as straight lines, however fine, of amazing narrowness, have a wonderful way of showing up from great distances, he would see the arterial roads leading to these stains. Anyone aware of plant growth would suspect that here they were presented with some sort of low lichen, but one that spread a fine filament-system of roots over the surface of the ground to feed it. To understand this one form of rather ill-ordered and obviously rudimentary living organism he, the explorer, would watch with care these rootlets. Even if they did not grow quickly enough for that growth to be seen, you might detect some kind of circulation of fluid going to and fro in these veins. And the observer would have been rewarded. Minute objects did slowly percolate up and down these fine channels.

Coming close to study this, the first signs of life in an otherwise apparently dead world, the watcher would next perceive the nature of these crawling protoplasms or germs or circulatory free-moving cells. He would see, as curiosity drew him daringly closer to the surface of the planet, that they were low organisms, crouched close on the fine runway or duct. He would then perhaps be close enough to see that, though they moved very slowly, they could not keep going for long. They evidently became exhausted, yawned open along their sides, discharged the contents of their digestive system, closed again their mouths or vents and fell to sleep. When they had recovered from their temporary exhaustion, they would suck into them again—or maybe devour—some smaller creature. After this their strength would come back to them and they would bumble off down the circulation ducts—so serving in their blind way the much vaster organism in which they lived and moved.

This discovery of the slowness, the weakness and the earth-boundedness of the things that moved in the ducts of the low and sprawling stain-organism, would make the observer fairly certain that these micro-organisms could not be either very strong nor very intelligent. Crouched on the earth, able to proceed—and then only on all-fours—only along these fine ducts, surely such creatures would have no interest save in what came straight in front of their down-bent noses. They would have luminous eyes with which they would see their way at night, but these eyes would be turned almost always on to the earth.

But then, having decided that this was the one species with which a visitor would have to deal, the newcomer would suddenly discover there was another species—a kind of rudimentary flying or air-skidding insect. And, what is more, there seemed some evidence that this insect did take an interest in things above it. Was it possible that it had noticed us, the cautious, far-distance-keeping visitors? Hardly possible for such a rudimentary animal! But then those who come on new facts must, above all, keep open minds. Nothing must be ruled out, in an unknown situation, however improbable, however ludicrous it must appear to a creature of commonsense. Of course, then, the first wise step is to plot the paths—and so deduce the powers and may be the purpose of the winged (or fluked) species. The crouched, crawling species had to have routes, ducts in which to creep.

Did the air-skidding creatures also have to follow lines, because, one might suggest, they had to be drawn along fine filaments from point to point ? They were a rarer species than the crawling lice or circulation cells of the earth level ducts. But it was soon clear that they nearly always were moving from one stain-patch to another—yes, they were on some kind of traffic schedule between these stains. Maybe they were a kind of fly that was thus cross-fertilising the lichen-stains? Perhaps they flew from one to another to collect its pollen. Certainly above the stain-organisms could generally be seen a kind of dust that might well be a discharge of fine reproductive spores on which the insects might live. In exchange they would blindly serve the purposes of the great main-plant-organisms by mixing the pollen of one distant plant with the pollen of another—a blend which the plant-organisms on their own could never hope to achieve.

So the first thing to do when this important discovery was made was, above all, to study the routes of these air-skid insects. As we have seen this nearly led to some accidents—though that may be going too far. In such perfect control of such perfect craft these riders of the upper sky may not have been taking the slightest risk.

If our grandparents or great-grandparents saw us 'weaving' along in our cars on the densely trafficked streets, the whole pelting stream often surging brightly along at thirty miles an hour, they would have gone home and had a quiet and final nervous break-down. To them a modern street could only be a picture of perpetual temptation of Providence, a nightmare of men continually, wantonly, risking instant destruction.

But there can be little doubt that these the visitors were learning.

They must keep away from us: give us a wider berth than perhaps they had thought at first they would have to give. But that was merely negative self-advice.

Could they do anything positive? Obviously. Was it not clear that the insect species had some kind of energy, may be tapped-power, perhaps no more than a higher protein-diet, that gave them the force to get up, if only into the lower thicker air—while all the rest of the living creatures either had to crawl along ducts, or lower still—if larger—just sprawl immobilised as did the big stain-organisms.

So the next step would be to find out what were these sources of power. How could the onlooker do that? Even human advance has in the last decade suggested a way, perhaps *the* way. In the last few years increasing use of the plane has been made for surveying for ores, mineral deposits, oil field possibilities. Instead of stumbling across the rough terrain, trying with heavy instruments to locate radiation coming from the ground, trying with such super-balances as the Etvos machine, attempting with gravimetric methods to gauge what masses of coal or other mineral may be under our feet, it has been found that instruments can be carried in planes that, riding in the air over such districts, give most useful readings to suggest what is hidden in the earth below. Let us suggest that the 'brooder' that hung for two days unmolested over Alice, Texas, was such an observer. Maybe he was making soundings in the earth 5,000 feet below him and maybe another 1,000 feet into the crust. Texas is one of the richest mineral sites in the world. Already it has given us much oil. There may be ores in that great district, ores the power possibilities of which we are yet too backward to know. The visitor may then have been making his soundings to answer the question: How are the earth-creatures—at least the winged species, powered, what is their food or fuel? As we have seen, our apparent resentment at such quiet investigation led the visitors to be more circumspect. But can we think they would abandon all hope of learning of our sources of power? Not till they know those can they safely approach a creature of uncertain intelligence and even more uncertain temper.

And, final speculation—for till we know more we must explore every possibility—might not this not unnatural supposition as to rationally cautious behaviour account for the one disaster that has marked this Saga of the Skies? Might it not account for the Kentucky tragedy? Fort Knox, which seems to have been in the centre of this episode, is, as was remarked above, the place where the greatest accumulation of gold was ever deposited by man. It has been guarded as if national safety depended upon it.

The late President Franklin Roosevelt had the grand old-fashioned fancy about Element 79 (gold), whose chemical symbol is AU and whose atomic weight used to be given as 197.2, but of whose unique value in chemistry or physics there is no evidence. Its worth, of course, is that it was, and still is, fairly rare and was once thought, but is no longer thought, to give a dead man a better chance of living in another world than the other poor fellow, who had none of it put in his dead mouth, could hope to have. Hence the oddest dump on the whole surface of this planet.

Can we doubt that any sky surveyor seeking to know of our powers and power resources, our ores, minerals and raw materials would not sooner or later strike the radiation, or gravitational displacement, of this huge dump? But its existence and its treasured care would awake further speculation, further puzzlement. Why do we keep that yellow junk? Do we circulate it? No. Do we eat it? No. Can it be used as a secret form of power generator? *That* must be it! So they would make their readings. It must be radio-active. Perhaps the creatures have found some method to get propulsive power out of it. After all one must never underrate strangers. Perhaps, after all, on one or two points, one of the species is really quite advanced. But still the gold refuses to give up its secret, still it remained stubbornly inexplicable—of no use, none whatsoever, completely inexplicable to any intelligent creature that did not know the tragic, bewildered, fantastic story of man's illusions and mistakes, misapprehensions and murderous muddles.

How could any creature of understanding hope to grasp the story of our insane fancy about AU, Element 79? How could he think that to-day, when we have flying and power sources, we still tie ourselves to a superstition which we do not even any longer believe? But to support the theory that these visitors may very well be plumbing and testing our power resources, we have at least more than a couple of strands of suggestion and deduction. This possible knowledge has come through Radar—our latest instrument for testing what we cannot see.

Radar, as everyone interested in it now knows, not only tells you of planes that have not yet arrived, of shoals of fish in the sea and where you may catch them, of raindrops falling in the height of the sky, of meteors as they fly invisibly by day and of their long tails and trains when even at night they have faded from view. But Radar also tells us of things that never turn up to our eyes—naturally we would expect that. After all, what we have just been talking of makes that not only likely, but certain. If with electric instruments you can tell, by the radiation which water gives off where it lies underground, where oil and coal and iron may be 1,000 and more feet below, then why not detect radiations that come from outside the earth? Of course thunderstorms, even when they are not booming and crashing, now give themselves away to Radar and indeed to many ordinary radio sets.

But there are some radiations, Radar findings, that awake speculation as to whether there could not be an intelligence, a probing intelligence, behind these rods and lines of force, these ultra-visible objects that send back the 'echo' that Radar picks up. In this case one of the most popular articles on the problem was issued by *The Saturday Evening Post*—the very paper that tried to pooh-pooh out of existence the discs themselves. On 6th March 1948 —while the saucers were very much—(and still to be)—on men's tongues and in their minds—the *Post* published a startling story under the heading, startling enough in itself, "The Sky is Haunted". No question-mark to give you a chance to doubt it. Flat statement.

These 'objects' which Radar has been picking up, mainly over North California, the author of the article calls 'Gizmos'. On one occasion the Radar picked up, and gave full indication of the fact that a plane must be crossing the flying field on which it, the Radar, was being operated. It gave the marks that are the signs that a plane is being echo-sounded and that it is a plane and not a shower of rain or a storm. If there was no living intelligence directing this invisible point or beam, then the focus would move with the wind. But these 'Gizmos' don't.

So it may be that we are being probed—which is precisely what we should expect of super-flyers—probed by their detection rays. And it is when our Radar comes up against these foci and shafts of invisible force that it gives off the signal which it utters when it strikes a solid object. For we must remember that the hardest radiation that we know, the radiation that comes from the cosmic deep of the outer sky, is so hard that we cannot feel it. That radiation rushes through our bodies, disturbing—Sir James Jeans told the present writer—probably not more than a couple of hundred of the trillions of atoms that make up our mortal frames. It rushes through matter as light through a window and has to go hundreds of feet—perhaps the hardest goes thousands—before it is checked. So these rods and foci of force that the Radar picks up, directed force, may be from the discs.

Now, granted that they must want to find out our sources of power—to understand our natures and capacity—they would direct their detectors wherever they found a great dump of any element. At Fort Knox they could hope to find the most refined and the most accumulated dump of gold that is or has ever existed. This then must be our real source of power! Marvellous to say, in this respect we—we may assume them to think—are ahead of them— at least from their generously cautious point of view, which concedes, when someone does something that seems to be absolutely stupid, that it cannot be as stupid as that, and so may be ultra-clever. But none of the instruments which the smaller discs carried could find out the radio-active, the power-aspect and potentiality of the great dump of gold. No doubt, night after night, they tried, and brought back to high-up headquarters again and again a blank. Two things were possible—perhaps it was screened in some way; perhaps at night it was protected or immune from the probes?

At least one more assault ought to be made on the problem, and in day-time. At least one ought to bring all one's guns of detection and probes of diagnosis to bear on this, the hardest nut, the most mysterious problem that earth had as yet given them to crack. Perhaps the most powerful detectors are too massive to be mounted safely on the hundred-foot discs, or borne in the long black hundred-foot length tubes. Perhaps the super-mother-ship, perhaps what may be the artificial satellite that, perchance, rides out on our orbit, alone carries the plant that could range and probe the riddle of the gold.

Then of necessity, they would bring down their monster ship. It would come rushing over; and, after the great swoop, go back to its high station, where, maybe, it rides three or four hundred miles or more, sweeping round us like a swift, minute, cryptic moon. But, alas, the story ended with miscalculation—one that probably could not have been foreseen, but one that may have led to even more caution on their part, as it did lead to more alarm on ours.

Here then we ought to ask another question: Are such notions as an artificial satellite quite absurd? The answer is "Certainly not". This step toward outer space and, say, a journey to the moon (off which, it must be remembered, quite a good echo has already been caught) has, as its first planned step, that we should mount a minute model satellite of our own. The plans are already being worked out. The Nazis were working on it as their super-siege-gun to fire down on their foes.

Now the Defence Centre at the great building in Washington D.C. called the Pentagon, has definitely announced the U.S. Earth Satellite Vehicle Programme. The man-constructed Satellite is to get out to its station by means of its rockets which will boost it aloft. It must go over 20,000 miles per hour to get free of the earth's pull. But it will not be sent nor allowed to go very far, so far as space is concerned. At 500 miles out, its automatic guiding gear will switch it round at right angles. The rockets will then cease to drive it and, spinning on its course, as does the moon on its circular path a quarter of a million miles farther out, our first contribution to the solar system, this earth-child, will rush round and round us. It will travel round our girth in a couple of hours. Then, when that is established, we are, so the plan goes, to plant another stepping-stone farther out on "the printless skies". This second base might act as a dock for other craft, which would launch out from this floating jetty and plunge into the real depths, wherein the bright and immense Earth will shrink to a watery gleam of light in the fabulous darkness, or a mote of blackness against the blinding welter of the unscreened Sun that drenches all our orbit with an unceasing blaze which evening or night never relieves.

Such are our notions, such what we feel to be our rational if high ambitions—though beside them the building of Babel seems a modest proposition, and "the overweening pride" which Aeschylus diagnoses as the cause of the Persian King's disaster (because he tried to chain the Hellespont)—such pride seems a very little thing.

But, if we consider that our own ground (and still mainly grounded) forces are thinking of scaling the sky and taking their stand outside even the atmosphere, we cannot be surprised, we should not be shocked, if we should find that we have been forestalled, and that someone else has already taken post on this desirable location with its unrivalled view of landscape and seascape.

So now we may know that we have some notion, if only the sketchiest, of the sky-cruisers' crews' viewing-stations, viewing powers and views. Of course they must have soon learnt that our automobiles did not really move themselves, were not really automatic. They were not carapaced insects. But we, the true motivators and living units, were these cars' still smaller slower and frailer inmates. So, too, with our planes.

But our powers? These still remained baffling. What could be our real forces? They would soon have detected our dependence on steam and oil. But must they not by now have suspected something much more disquieting? However disproportionate it must seem to our puny controls, our feeble bodies, must it not be suspected by a looker-on, must not his radar probes continually suggest that places such as Oak Ridge in the States or Harwell in Britain have an alarming reaction note, a forbidding radiation? Of the direction in which such suspicions would, and indeed must, point, we shall be having to look when, once again, with our further accumulation of deductive knowledge both of Craft and Crews, we re-open the question 'Whence?'

Before that we must ask another preliminary Craft-Crew question. Granted that the smaller discs come down from a giant disc riding now as our second (and very midget) moon right under our lee, could a whole swarm of visitors have such a base? What was viewed once and perhaps twice was a monstrous enough thing — perhaps 1,000 feet across. Nevertheless, is that large enough to act as the floating jetty for crews to man say a thousand and more craft many a hundred feet across? To ask a human crew of a whole flotilla to lie-up and rest-out in one mother ship of such a size would be the cruellest congestion. But congestion bears an exact inverse relation to size. The first gets less as the second gets larger.

It is here then that we must raise again an important piece of Craft evidence as throwing light on Crew build. Here we had a startling, and at the time apparently anomalous, piece of expert witnessing, which now has a strange appositeness. We recall that at the White Sands observations Commander MacLaughlin remarked, as a trained observer would and could, that there were two acute problems raised by the flight of the saucers as the observing teams checked it. The first was the tremendous speed—18,000 miles per hour, and on top of that, and even more serious, the tremendous acceleration. Nothing larger than an insect, say a bee, could stand that sheer push, and not literally be pushed out of life, pushed out of its body. And yet, and this is the second point, the Commander felt that, considering the way the discs were handled and turned, it seemed unavoidable to conclude that they were under direct control of inmates, that they were 'manned'.

So we must assume that the masters of these machines are minute. What they may mean by and large we can wait a moment to see, while we fit this answer, as far as we have it, to the question which demanded it:— Could a disc, only 1,000 feet across, act as the rest home and holiday-ground for crews that 'man' whole fleets of discs? To an insect, of course, a residence 1,000 feet across would not merely be a city, it would be a whole county a whole province, a state in itself.

Chapter XI
WHENCE AGAIN?

NOW we must go back to 'Whence?' armed with a little more knowledge. We cannot any longer decline or oppose the thrust of the question, Where, if not Here? The force of the argument drives us out, if we cannot find purchase for the discs on earth. We have searched the whole of the land and suspected even the sea; some people have suggested that the discs rise from the ocean and take to the sky, disliking only earth. This attempt to do without the hyphen of the solid between liquid and gas, seems a hopeless effort to avoid the difficulty of finding the discs some base. None of the earth or ocean sites will hold water.

We are forced up into the air; and the facing up to the artificial satellite is of course only a stepping stone, (as the thing itself must be) to get our minds, as the crews aloft get their bodies, to some extra-terrene goal. If it was not sent up, then it must have come down. It must be like that manipulatory midget world that Jonathan Swift imagined as the Kingdom of Laputa, in Gulliver's Travels, which could be raised and lowered by its inhabitants. Anyhow, as we are being forced out to ever great distances and heights by the force of argument and evidence, let us, too, do some viewing and scanning. If we must leave home, let us start on the sunny side of space. But the first and sunniest spot certainly will not do.

Life may exist under the strangest of conditions. Sir Spencer Jones, the Astronomer Royal, has said that bodies might be constructed not from carbon, as ours mainly are, but with silica as a base, resisting heats which would be deadly to us. But Mercury, the innermost planet, has on its sunny side a temperature that would melt lead. If you could stand that, why have a body at all? There may be creatures in the sun, but they must be fields-of-force, electric vortices, subtle bodies, what you will—but not beings that need to man space-ships. We leave, then, Mercury, after one almost blinding glance, and take refuge on Venus.

With Venus serious enquiry begins; and, indeed, what is such a help to serious enquiry, a proper sequence—everyone knows it. The sequence runs Venus, Earth, Mars. Most people believe it is a chronological sequence: Venus young, ourselves middle-aged, Mars old. But Venus is too young. It is amazing what is now known about our neighbours, especially these two, one on our inner and the other on our outer side.

The first thing, of course, is to try to find out what perhaps you will first see. If there are clouds, you will first see them. And if they are dense, that is all you will see. And they are dense, unrelievedly dense, on Venus. They have once or twice been seen to eddy but never to break. Their bright blank blanket turns back all our peering. But we can turn our spectroscopes on that bright screen. And that does tell us something, something that seems pretty final. That blanket is not the cloud, the white cloud that we know of our own sky. It is made of carbon-dioxide. It is not to be unexpected. If Venus is much younger than us, or perhaps we should say, because nearer the Sun, later to cool, slower to clear, then of course she should have that kind of clotted atmosphere made of that kind of gas. For carbon-dioxide is a very favourable gas, or air, for planets, but not for animals; least of all for a 'brainy' animal that needs oxygen. As the carbon-dioxide diminished in our atmosphere, it would seem the great masses of vegetable growth that were laid down as the coal-measures, withered away for good. And in their stead came more and more animals, more and more active, more and more interested in looking at what was now appearing clearly, the sky and the stars. For that fact, or the negative side of it, would alone tell against a 'Venusian' being a space explorer. For you cannot explore what you have never thought about nor believed to exist. Even if a fish-like creature swimming in a hot swamp, even if an intelligent Venus fly-trap (a plant which can catch insects) thought of leaving home, where would its thoughts go? Above there is nothing but a cloud, so thick that its underside, like the hearts of our great dazzling-topped cumuli are found to be, may be almost dead-dark; and, anyhow, all round must be steam and fog that may reduce visibility to a few yards. If you never can see more than a foot or two, your eyes are apt to have that modest range, granted that you have eyes at all.

So we must leave Venus, as we left Mercury. The one would give us too much light; the other too little. And finally we find ourselves confronted with Mars. Of course there is something a little vulgar, we now feel, about the notion. We all would like to avoid it. For a couple of generations we have been having Messages from Mars—from popular plays which were so heavy with Moral that Mars, it was clear, was only a mixture of a catapult and a pulpit, a place from which it was hoped to launch, with the impetus and surprise of novelty, a message so old that, as John Morley said, it could only be classified among the Eternal Commonplaces. And Commonplaces are not made any less common by being given uncommon places as pretence entrances.

After the popular plays, or indeed alongside them, came the first science-fictions. H. G. Wells brought in Mars with a dash. But of course, being a very bellicose little man, he had to make it a War of the Worlds, and the Martians themselves squids of the most squiggling horror, whose one use for human beings was to suck their blood. It was a blood-and-bones, heat-ray and pandemic business from first to last. We had nothing to hope from the Martians: they nothing to do with us but to drain us dry and inherit the earth.

Naturally the Astronomers—who are generally benign men, whose blood, not being frozen by the thought of the cold of outer space, is not likely to be chilled by the fancies of amateurs—did not like that sort of thing. They, too, had become used to wandering about in the utterly empty and vacant Universe—some with God and some without. What they did not wish, and saw no need to invite it, was that any other creature should share their solitude. Probably a psychologist would tell us that men become astronomers because they have at heart no love for life, but enjoy being a disembodied eye which refers all its findings to a purely mathematic ego. If you are used to having all the garden to yourself, even if it is very large and very bare, you resent the thought of intruders and indeed of anyone that you did not introduce.

Undoubtedly the vast number of astronomers were inclined to say "Certainly Not" to any common person who said, "Could there not be life on Mars?" And when Lowell, the Harvard astronomer, having gone to Flagstaff, Arizona, for the very clear air, said that he had seen canals, and was sure that they were periodically flooded by intelligent creatures to irrigate their crops, then all but one or two of the profession said, "We have never seen any of these lines that you say are there." It was therefore perhaps a visit of courtesy that a disc appeared over Flagstaff, there to show itself to Dr. Hess, who now keeps the watch set by Dr. Lowell with such romantic energy and exciting speculation.

Before then we dare open again this somewhat inflamed question and see how the controversy (sometimes called the Battle of Mars) has gone, we had better, for peace sake, look at all the 'rest-spots' or 'bases' in our system. Out beyond Mars of course is a belt of asteroids, 'The Asteroids'. They are no use to us as they are—Ceres, the largest measured so far, is a mere raft of a thing. More than 1,000 have been spotted. Some competent calculators think there may be fifty times that number. What they were once, what astronomers have mainly agreed they come from, we shall be coming to in a moment. It has a possible bearing—quite a strong one—on our tale.

On again. In our search we come to Jupiter and Saturn, the two Giants. We know what their atmosphere is. It is probably frozen: it is with high certainty Methane Gas, utterly suffocating to any animal life we associate with intelligence. Under that more than Arctic Sea of frozen methane it is hard to think of anything that we know as life breaking out or keeping on. Uranus, Neptune, Pluto and perhaps a hither-Pluto, a final Proserpine—what of these? Further cold, further darkness, further uncertainty of anything that would guide us to a home of life. Sir James Jeans told the writer that if there was a being on Pluto and he was looking for sunrise he would have to search the sky carefully—granting that the sky was visible at all on that planet—to be sure that the Sun had risen. Among the stars and the larger nearer planets the Sun might appear only as a star among other stars.

So, having wandered to the rim of the solar system, why should we go farther? After having been told for years that the Sun alone with any probability had planets, we are now informed that plenty of stars probably have them. Very well, but why start searching out there for planets—deduced and never seen—upon which life might possibly exist and from which, therefore, visitors might come (when they have their own system to explore first), when we still have one awkward applicant waiting to be examined. So back, however unwillingly, to Mars!

As soon as we do get back—that is to the latest current findings made by experts looking at Mars, we do find a change of 'climate' a warmer feeling toward the Red Planet, a hint and more than a hint that the gap between the Lowellians, the canal-speculators, and their severe critics may, if it be not closing, at least no longer have such yawning and abrupt edges.

We left Mars with the vast majority of astronomers and especially the greater part of the Mars experts saying, "The place is quite impossible, please do not trouble us with offers to show that it could be a good building site for life."* The 'Noes' held the floor of the astronomic debating house. They took their stand first on general principles.

What is Mars, if we are to trust our senses? Well, when we have used the best helps to our eyes which, twenty years ago,

* Note: Even those basic astronomers who are content just to measure and weigh (planets are naturally their favourite game) have changed their mind about Mars. From Dr. H. Jeffreys, holding Mars to be very different in mass from the Earth, though W. H. Ramsey maintained that it was considerably different, we have now Dr. K. E. Bullen and then Dr. W. H. Ramsey (*Monthly Notes of the Royal Astronomical Society, 1949 and 1950*) maintaining that Mars is not 'discrepant', and that it has an inner core in the same proportion as the Earth carries. Further, its core is, like ours, very massive and probably made as ours is supposed to be made, of nickel iron. This, of course, has a very considerable bearing on the question raised above when discussing the powering of the discs. For only a people long acquainted with magnetism—through the magnetic nature of their own native planet—would be likely to discover magnetic power as a means of interplanetary motion and a method of 'defying gravitation'—in other words the secret of how you may hover as long as you like.

telescopes could give, we saw an object about the size of a small gooseberry and of the tint that the reddish variety of that fruit often shows, tawny with slight stains of a greenish hue. But any photograph did show something that no gooseberry wears, even when mildewed.

The Poles of Mars had white caps. The hopefuls at once said, "That's snow—just as our planet would show, if we from Mars were looking at Earth". The conservatives counter-attacked—"No, it is frozen carbon-dioxide; and so, if you were on Mars, you would be in no condition, and would never have reached any condition, in which you could think of being curious from your station on Planet Four about the nature and possibilities, the life and possible intelligence on Planet Three!"

"Then what about the greenish patches? Surely these are vege-tation, and vegetation might mean animal life?"

"No, again!" said the opposers. "You must not make assump-tions and interpolate your own incurable anthropomorphism! The green could be merely chemical changes—after all, corrosion often gives a green patina to red-looking metals and their dust — think of copper and verdigris! There is no water above ground—no flash of lagoon or lake. The dirty green patches are the graves of oceans, and the grave of the ocean is the tomb of life—for life came out of the sea, and when the sea goes life vanishes too!".

"But there are clouds!"

"Most—the large, dark ones—are just dreadful dust devils—rust particles whirling about in devastating tornadoes".

"But there are white ones".

"They are made simply of a superfine snow".

Here we must pause and ask, How can all this be known when you are watching a thing that at best is a poor sort of cherry? Have we got finely enlarged photographs? We have not, and will not have for a year or two more. Why not? Because of those subtle twister-devils of our own atmosphere—the convection currents, the wavering of warm or hot air as it rises, a wavering which distorts any image seen through it. The image of Mars is never steady long enough for our present plates to take a perfectly clear photograph.

We do depend—and that has made the canal controversy so difficult and even bitter—because we *have* to depend—on drawings made by astronomers, as moment by moment, for an instant, the image clears and we see with a clarity that the photographic plate is too slow to record.

Well, then, is not everything speculation, and critics and believers all in the same boat of drifting ignorance? No. For even before the huge hundred-inch telescope was brought to bear on our Mars mystery (and even it has not been able to give us a clear photograph —for that we are waiting on and from the 200-inch mirror when Mars next comes close), the spectroscope and the thermocouple had got to work on the problem.

The spectroscope of course is a magic resolver of chemical questions. Hence the judgment whether Mars has—or has not— oxygen and carbon-dioxide can be settled more or less by this means. The thermocouple can tell what the temperature is on the surface of the planet. Of course, these tests, as they have gone on, have told not wholly in favour of the "Noes", who deny the exist- ence of life there.

First and foremost the spectroscope showed that the caps were not frozen carbon-dioxide but true frozen water—the very way they melt in the Martian Spring shows that this is water—not dry ice melting—or one should say water melting, for dry ice does not 'melt', it vaporises straight away from solid to gas.

But the Noes counter-attacked: "The Caps are simply hoar- frost!—their spectrum shows that. Try to irrigate with the flow from hoar-frost!"

"But the green patches do get green and lose their sere appear- ance when the Spring comes on and the polar cap melts!"

"Ah, but we have two nice back-handers for your hopes on this very point. The thermocouple gives you one and the spectroscope gives you the other. The thermocouple shows that the heat is actually greater above the green patches than on the red desert. Now everyone knows that air over a forest is *always* cooler than air over even ordinary open land, let alone a red desert! The buffet from the spectroscope is even more flooring—the spectro- scope shows that the so-called vegetation belts or patches do not give the same spectroscopic reaction that chlorophyll—the very substance and life-blood of all our vegetation—should give!"

Still there is a counter-counter-attack to this severe shock. At least the thermocouple's verdict of death can be reversed. For a Soviet astronomer (perhaps he had a loyalty to a red planet) showed from work on the farthest north spruces and other conifers that these trees which have to face sub-zero temperatures have already reacted to that danger by an amazing device. Their fine narrow 'leaves' actually can hold heat, and they, in point of fact, do create for themselves a blanket of warmth, to keep out the intolerable cold, under which they can survive. All we see in Mars is not an anomaly that opposes the hope of life, but as a matter of fact one of life's new victories, the beginning of which we are witnessing on our own frontier of utter cold.

Life is certainly far ahead of us on Mars. And we may ask, for the question is crucial and really decisive, if life down here started under the most favourable and protected conditions—in shallow sea-pools, near the shore, sheltered by warm mists—and then has gone on, under a clearing and 'colding' sky? What does that suggest? And further, if life has not only originated but, while conditions have become more strenuous, has climbed from the shore—as Beebe has shown, life has also dived into the black of the deep; and, as the Swedish Deep Ocean Expedition has shown, has gone right through the so called Azoic Abyss and, in the form of those animals called Daphnis, or sea-slugs, is now parading the seven-miles-down floor of the ultimate ocean—if life has gone down and up—why it is carrying the offensive against death, carrying the war right into the enemies' country!

Life is not losing, it is winning. That fact of the thermocouple's finding, interpreted in the light of what we now know about the offensive fight being carried on by our own trees against the Arctic sub-zero cold: that fact may help us, too, to answer the spectroscope, when it says these so called growths on Mars are not vegetation. For is chlorophyll the only 'life-blood' that a vegetable can use? Take our own blood, whose tint is given it by iron. The crustaceans also have a blood of a sort. Though it is red, they have made their crimson life-fluid out of a copper base.* It has also been suggested that there have been forms of life that used manganese as a base. There seems to have been a time in our own geological past when there were trees which had manganese in their constitution.

Finally, we have found that even in our own world there are forms of vegetation that do not use chlorophyll. We used to think that life had only one way of getting up to consciousness, one very narrow accidental crack or canyon in the blank face of things and that somehow by blind luck life leaked through, only to fail and perish at the top. But that picture does not seem at all inevitable. Convergence (the idea that life has made quite a number of shots and searchings to get through and up) is a notion inconvenient for those students who want a very simple plan to impose on things and help to order their actual findings. Convergence, there can be no doubt, is becoming an idea harder and harder to keep out of the text-books.

So there is no reason why there should not be life on Mars. The planet is farther out than we are—generally 50,000,000 miles farther out. There is no doubt it is ahead of us, and therefore could manage better with its more strenuously rationed resources than we could. It is also smaller than us and so would have gone more quickly through the first stages of its history.

But Mars is of the same substance as Earth, and that substance has nourished life. "Only vegetation, remember!" comes the warning voice. But has vegetation ever been found without mobile life—did they not both spring from the same root? Is not a yeast right at the division of the ways—can there be vegetation and not animal life? Are they not partners, are they not (to use the technical word) symbiots, that is to say co-operative companions tied in a perfect balance with one another?

That is the conclusion of most observers of Mars to-day. For there can be no doubt that gradually, in the past twenty years, the attitude that assumed life on Mars was the natural reaction of human sentimentality, is not anything like as definite as it was.

* Vanadium, a rare element, is nevertheless used by vast numbers of a small sea-creature to make its 'blood'.

Indeed, we may say that up to date—in the past three or four years—the 'Lifers' have won most informed opinion from the 'Non-lifers'.

"Yes," it is allowed, "there is vegetation".

Another Soviet astronomer has come in on this less-materialist side. He has added that the amount of carbon-dioxide that is found on Mars—or in its spectrum—is not as high as should be found if there were no vegetation, but is nicely adjusted with the balance that vegetable life would manage; for it is the vegetation's power of dealing with carbon-dioxide and the animal's power of dealing with oxygen that makes one of their strongest symbiotic ties and mutual services*

But what sort of animal (putting aside the question whether there could be a vegetable that was as intelligent as an animal) could exist on that desert? Dr. Gerard P. Kuiper of Chicago, who is one of the great authorities on the atmosphere of our fellow planets, said in the middle of March 1950—"No form of life as we know it could exist on Mars but insect life."

Now it is at this point that we reach a real crisis in this story. If there is vegetation, there is pretty certainly insect life. Plants and insects are nearly the first example that even the cursory study of Symbiosis and Ecology (the interbalance of a whole area's way of living) brings to light. Further, we know how far insects have gone with us. Three quite different branches of the vast tree of insect life have stretched up—each on its own account—and have achieved ways of social management, elaborate economies, masterly co-operation, triumphs of co-ordinated specialisation such as we thought, when we started to think of such things, were confined strictly to ourselves, to the great-brained creature called Man. The Ants, the Termites—which of course, though a dirty white, are not ants at all. They may have sprung from some sort of aspiring

* Professor B. A. Vorontsov-Velyaminov has declared that the atmosphere on Mars contains approximately the same percentage of carbon-dioxide as that on the Earth, while Dr. Tikhov pointed out that there must be plant life on Mars because without plant life the carbon-dioxide content would be much higher. We know that it is because plant-life can absorb carbon dioxide and give out oxygen that is is possible for us to get the oxygen we need and not be asphyxiated by the C.O.2 we breath out.

cockroach. Thirdly and most familiar to us (because of its long-superior power of making what we need, sugar) is the Bee, the Honey-bee.

The Ants have slaves and 'cows', they till a fungus crop and forage and store. The only creatures except ourselves to do so, they have real wars, and capture and enslave their captives.

The Termites are even more acute. Actually running ahead of our wildest 'Eugenists', they breed soldiers, mighty warriors to defend their castles, special trap-mouthed creatures which can cut an invader in half with their huge jaws.

In the studies that in the past fifty years have been made of the Ants and the Termites, it seemed that the poor Bee was being left behind. We had thought that it was the perfect model of efficient self-effacing industry. Of course there was the Ant; but the Bee was better. But now the Ant and the Termite seem even more industrious, more self-effacing—though the by-product of the one is not honey but only ants' eggs (only useful for those who keep gold-fish and some other fanciers); and the by-product of the other is (if you live where they work) the dust of your whole house, eaten out over your head and from under your feet; for wood, not flowers, is the diet of the Termite.

In any case the insects have given us many surprises. They are intelligence incarnate, in a way most surprising, and even a little disquieting. What if they should wish to take over? Be assured, the entomologists have replied, they cannot. They took the wrong turn long, long ago. They did not evolve lungs. They breathe through holes all over their bodies. This is a very crude way of respiring. It has therefore one great handicap (luckily for us)—it limits their size.

The insect can never grow large. One of the largest is the Tarantula Spider, perhaps as much as a couple of inches in length of body, or a little more. And we know the size of Bee, Ant and Termite. Not only does their size make them helpless against us, (their physique handicaps them hopelessly) but so do their minds. Ingenious they seem and no doubt are; but inventive, no; responsive to new conditions, never again.

Why? Because they settled down millions of years ago. Before we had even thought of thinking, they had done, for good and all, all of theirs. Their little, hard, encased bodies are not so hard and stiff and shut up as their little, instinct-bound and riveted minds. We can find in amber millions of years old, perfect examples preserved of ants which are just like the ants of to-day. Of course that argument has a little twist in it that we should note in passing. For, though their bodies may not have changed for geological ages, we cannot prove by that that their minds have not done so either.

If we take the skull of that paleolithic creature, Cro-Magnon man, we find that it is as lofty, wide and high, and as roomy inside, as ours. But did that person have our civilisation, did he have our ideas of power? He had not even the simplest agriculture. He seems to have been simply a hunter. We do not know that he had even a hut to live in. His mind, as shown by some contemporary art and tools, seems to have been at the level at which there comes 'eidetic imagery'—(that is, the images in your mind appearing to be objective pictures, seen, say, against a blank wall).

So, as our minds have grown enormously in the past twenty thousands of years (though our brains may still take up no more room) so, too, the minds of the Bees may have grown, though their brains are not larger than those of their ancestors. This is all the more likely when we remind ourselves that the more efficient a brain is the less, not the more room, it may take up. Early machines are always more clumsy, more diffuse than later and better ones. So with the human brain. We have discovered that it is the depth of the convulution that may give us better correlation of brain with mind than mere size. Some idiots have very large brains. Anatole France, one of the most brilliant of French authors, had a brain that was so small as to be close to that level usually associated with microcephalic idiots. But the convulutions, the foldings, were very deep.

Finally, when we consider that we know very far less about a Bee's brain than we do about our own—and our knowledge of our own brain has proved baffling in a number of cases—we must conclude that we can do little to study, still less to understand, a Bee's mind by looking at its brain. What we must do is what we do with ourselves when we want to gauge intelligence: we watch how the mind works that is using the body—what can it do, design, create?

We know that Bees have come a long way by that test. It is pretty certain that they started with a far simpler way of life than now is theirs: as we started without gear and goods and plant and tools and cities and transport. It is generally conceded that the Bees, which have cities and an hierarchical society, came up from solitary forms, many of which still survive. They have built up cities and the organisation of cities, control of population, supply, distribution of power, and order of succession in a manner so masterly that besides it our own efforts look amateurish and dangerously incompetent.

But, say the critics with assured finality, all this is in vain. For Bees are hopelessly instinct-ridden. They really do not know how they do it and indeed they, the individual Bees, can do nothing about it and probably know nothing about it, about the whole process and economy, the plan and the polity. To the question, "Then who does?" the usual believer in 'instinct' gives a polite shrug of the shoulders. It is just vulgar anthropomorphism to ask what Instinct is. The word is final and closes the discussion.

As to the basic idiocy of the insects, even the most skilled of them, we are asked to look at the widely-publicised Sphex Wasp, whose absurdities so amused Fabre and many another naturalist. For this solitary wasp hovers uneasily on the edge of apparent intelligence—only and always to tumble off helplessly on the side of complete senselessness. We all know how it makes—true mason wasp that it is—a mud-cement nest for its egg which it hasn't yet laid: how, when the cell is ready, it lays the egg in the receptacle. Then off it goes to fetch a caterpillar to act as food for the grub which will come out of the egg in due time—a time that the mother will never see. That being so, the caterpillar must oblige by doing two things—it must stay still and wait to be eaten by the egg that has yet to become an eater, but it must not stay too still, that is, lie in state, dead; otherwise, by the time the eater had been hatched, the meal of caterpillar would have decomposed. The caterpillar is kept fresh and lively for its enemy by being stung in the hinder of its nerve ganglia, so that without refrigeration, but with the aid of paralysis, it will be preserved. This seems a perfect if grim procedure, showing a wonderful sense of provision. But—and this has been proved again and again—while the mother is off caterpillar-hunting you can remove the egg from the cell. You can watch; and, sure enough, the Sphex comes back with the caterpillar, and, never seeming to notice that the egg has gone—the *raison d'être* of the whole procedure—it walls up the caterpillar in the empty receptacle and then goes off content. It has good eyes, wonderful eyes. Yet so blinded is it by instinct, by absorption only with that part of the procedure it is intent upon, so ignorant is it of the whole process and purpose, that it just cannot see that it has been utterly frustrated.

It certainly is as pretty a demonstration of something having gone wrong with instinct, with race memory, as you could wish. But before we lift the example and apply it to the Bees, let us remember that here, with the Sphex, we are dealing with a solitary creature, a creature that went on with its racial pattern by itself and never attained to the elaboration of the social life of the Bees, Ants and Termites. They have evolved far, far away from the solitary state.

Back, however, comes the critic: "Look at Bees then; you will find really very little difference."

So most entomologists would have said until quite lately. Indeed, so certain had they become that all insects were incapable of anything that we would call consciousness, that J. Loeb, who was, forty years ago, one of the great entomologists, felt that it was unwise even to speak of instinct. Race memory, if that was what instinct was being taken to mean, was altogether too romantic a term. He popularised, for describing insect behaviour, the word Tropism. The insect turns towards its food—the pollen for the bee, the carrion for the carrion fly—because it is drawn compulsorily, drawn unconsciously, just as iron-filings are drawn to a magnet.

That was the standard faith. Then, after the First World War, an Austrian entomologist of high standing began to publish papers on bee behaviour—in which he was a specialist. The results have proved so revolutionary that it will be simplest and briefest to give here a short popular account written from the actual reports of Dr. K. Von Frisch's work. In the following pages are summarised the knowledge, up to date, about the intelligence of Bees. For if this is not intelligence, then it is hard to know in what sense to employ that word.

Today we have to face one further revolution on the Science Front. We had begun to think that all the great revolutions in thinking, all the radical changes in research-opinion, were in Physics. The proof that Matter is really Force (and vice versa) and that Alchemy (the Transmutation of the Elements) does take place, these facts upset and transformed the old 'Classical Physics'. And Physics was and is the basic Science, the 'tortoise' on which the others are carried.

But Biology and Psychology, the other two great divisions of Science, are much closer to us than Physics, and so seem to matter more. And they have so far refused to recognise the revolution in Physics as making any real difference to them. Psychology, as we know, has tried to find every excuse for not looking at Extra-sensory Perception, while Biology has mainly clung to a simple, old-fashioned, 'fundamentalist' materialism. Hence the violence of the shock when a great biologist, an entomologist, an apiologist (a specialist in bee behaviour) produces irrefragable evidence, confirmed by other observers, that bees *do* think, and can and do constantly exchange thoughts, consciously make plans, and compare information.

This revolutionary fact—quite as revolutionary in Biology as Alchemy was in Physics, and meaning more for us—must be faced. Bees actually speak. They continually converse with each other. As clearly as iip-readers carry on conversation, so can and does the Honey-bee. As plainly and definitely as we draw sketches and plans to direct each other (so as to find a street or house) so do these insects. How?

There are few bee-observers greater than Dr. Von Frisch. This astounding discovery is his. Only of late has it come to light. His first two papers were published in German in 1946 from where he was working in the Austrian countryside near Graz. The next two appeared in 1948 and 1949. It may seem amazing that Bees, which have been kept by man for millenia, should have been able to pass as dumb for so long. But when we look into the mystery we see why their secret was till now overlooked.

The Bees' sign-language is elaborate. Because it is so advanced and complex it long escaped detection. If you showed cursive Chinese or rapid short-hand to anyone used to reading only block capitals and unaware, not only of any other script, but of any other creature that could write, such a person might easily refuse to believe that the tangled strokes and dashes were anything but aimless scrawling. So, though plenty of people, generation by generation, had seen bees signalling to one another, they could not see that such capers *were* signals.

Bees have so much to say, they can convey such extensive and exact information, that for this very reason, if you do not from the start get the hang of it, you are completely at a loss. Fortunately the one subject they discuss is a simple one; the subject of all their conversation is honey. That is the master clue. Had they ever talked about anything else, had they, like ourselves, masses of irrelevant interests and amusements to distract them and elaborate their messages, then we still might not have realised that Bees do talk. For it is a shock. One ranking entomologist remarked when shown the von Frisch research papers, "I am almost passionately unwilling to accept this evidence." For Bees have been catalogued as 'creatures of instinct'. That means that they *cannot* think for themselves. But if you are continually giving exact instructions about places and distances to your fellows, you are thinking, and so are they.

The actual signs and signals, which the discoverer of the Bee language has noticed, catalogued and interpreted, had already been noticed by many bee-keepers. Anyone who keeps a hive can do this. But such signals seemed quite insignificant. Every now and then, when a foraging Bee comes into the hive, instead of unloading at once its nectar or pollen, it fusses about, fidgets, quivers and circles aimlessly. "Excess of motivational urge" said the old observers: a sort of short-circuiting of energy due to over-stress.

But von Frisch noticed that the adjacent Bees did not seem either impatient or indifferent to this display. On the contrary, they seemed attentively interested; what was more, they apparently learned something and acted on it. For von Frisch had put his hives in country where there were no other bee-keepers. Unless he had done this he never could have begun to unravel this most unlikely riddle, a mystery so disguised that we never suspected its existence.

But that was only the first necessary step. The second, which was as necessary, was to mark each separate Bee with a small spot of distinctive paint. Then as soon as he began to suspect that the insects were actually communicating, von Frisch guessed that the only subject about which they would talk about would be honey, or the raw material for it. So he placed, at various distances from the hive, caches of sugar. He found quickly that it was always a Bee that had discovered such a dump which straightway cut these queer capers on returning to the hive. Further, those Bees that watched her, after a few moments flew out of the hive and went straight for the hidden treasure. Of course this could still be explained away as the pioneer's elation exciting the others, which seeing that she was loaded with loot, rushed out, and by luck lit on the deposit she first had located.

But year-by-year experiment convinced von Frisch that he must abandon all these simpler, less startling explanations. He placed his sugar caches miles from the hives and yet the Bees went straight for them. There could be no doubt that they must have been given exact information. He therefore noted with increasing care every movement of the capering Bee on its return from finding a cache.

First it milled around—it described a circle. That was followed by a more confusing behaviour. At last he got the hang of it. Across the circle that she had described, the discoverer was now pacing out a bisecting line. It was not all easy to recognise this. For when the Bee so performed, she appeared to be so excited that the performance seemed more a tipsy dance than a steady piece of measuring. Her whole body waggled and squirmed. No wonder any former observers of this trick had dismissed the whole thing as aimless excitement.

Von Frisch's great discovery lay in recognising that in all this pirouetting there was the most precise pointing. In brief, he has proved, and convinced other entomologists, that the Bee, when drawing this diagonal across the circle, is giving the onlooking Bees the direction in which lies the cache. If the food-place lies in a straight line between the hive and the sun, then the Bee paces straight up the comb. If the sugar-mine lies straight away from the sun, when the sun is straight behind the hive, then she paces straight down the comb. If the cache is to right or left of the line made by the sun and the hive, she indicates on which side and at what angle, by the slant at which she cuts across the circle she has described.

But how does she know where the sun is when it is overcast, or when from the hive she can only see a narrow glimpse of the sky? That led to a further discovery. The Bee, it appears, can see polarised light. The atmosphere polarises the sunlight a little. Some people have eyes that permit them to see this. The Bee sees these 'streakings' across the sky and from them—as we should do from the beams of a search-light—she estimates where the sun actually is.

But why, if she is being so intelligent, so precisely informative in giving the line and pointer to reach the food-place, must she confuse the whole thing by such waggling and squirming that till now no one suspected that she was conveying exact bearings? Surely concluded von Frisch, if the Bee is so unwaveringly efficient a worker, such a persistently rational creature, she would not be wasting time and energy and risk confusing her fellows unless there were method in her procedure.

Here, sure enough, von Frisch came upon his super-discovery. For, whereas her circling and diagonalling gave the direction-line to the onlookers, the way she wobbled and squirmed as she went up and down that line gave the distance away at which the store would be found. Von Frisch counted carefully with a stop-watch the number of these waggles of the abdomen and he found that from them he could make a scale which indicated the space between the hive and the cache! The Bee is a perfect 'timer' and her fellow-bees can and do count! For it is precisely the number of complete 'waggle-dances', that she taps off in a definite period of time, that tells the actual distance the store lies from the hive.

The Bee is so ingenious, so consciously intelligent, so aware of the way that her information must be given to her companions, that she actually gives her estimate, not (as we used to imagine she always flew) 'in a bee-line', but making allowances for the actual distance flown when it is necessary to go out of the way—for instance, in order to round a hill which it would be needlessly exhausting to fly over.

It is then that Bee (and only that Bee) which has found a really outstanding deposit, does, on arriving on the comb (or sometimes even on the alighting board) call the others' attention by describing the circle. and pacing out the round. Then, by diagonalling the circle, she tells them in what direction the deposit lies. Thirdly, by the rhythms of her body movements, as she goes along the indicator line, she conveys to the spectators how far they will have to fly.

They clinch the proof by starting out straightaway. They follow precisely her instructions and find the treasure-trove.

That this is real thinking and exchange of information cannot any longer be doubted. When we consider (i) The recalling by the Bee of the distance she has travelled; (ii) The calculations of direction she must make, by establishing the triple position of hive, sun and cache; (iii) The transposition of the map in her mind (the actual picture of the countryside) which is of course horizontal, to the vertical plane of the hive-comb—then we can no longer refuse to believe that Bees talk, Bees draw maps, and Bees can read what a map-drawer sketches. It is a complete revolution of all our former notions of what an insect's consciousness could possibly be.

There must then remain one most disturbing but also most exciting question. If Bees can talk and do exchange detailed information about their business, would it not be possible to discover whether they ever talk about other things? For example, do they plan defences when they are being attacked by their many enemies? The badger sometimes launches an attack on them; ants are their enemies; some birds, such as the woodpecker, are not out for their honey, but like to eat *them*. The skunk will sit under a hive and, if the alighting board is low, go on licking up the entering bees (wrapping them in his sticky saliva so that they cannot sting his throat or mouth) until at length he will deplete a whole hive.

Against all these enemies Bees try to make counter-attacks; and when the hive itself is assaulted they show the power of co-ordinated strategy and tactics that one would expect of intelligence. Of course it would be hard to detect this war-councilling—for then the hive is under the strictest martial law and an eavesdropper could be regarded only as a spy—to be shot at sight.

We would have then to seek for an opening for negotiation when things are quiet. Surely they may have noticed that we are sometimes highly convenient—that we can be of honey-use. It may be because they recognise this in some people that toward such they are friendly, as we know they are to some bee-keepers.

If once they could get over the immense initial obstacle that makes them assume that we are hopelessly stupid and incapable of serious, sustained attention (but are really as brainless, rapacious, disordered and repulsive as badgers) why should we not exchange signals? It would be a greater discovery than breaking the atom, to break through into a Bee's mind and learn what the world looks like from the Bee's point of view. It might prove more than an idle investigation, the converse of teaching a parrot to talk. It might, as we shall see in a moment, prove to be the most useful lesson we could take in a foreign language, the most valuable 'other tongue' that we have ever mastered.

We used to be told that half our international difficulties would disappear if only we could talk to strangers—talk to people of 'the other side'. The late George Lansbury, the gallant old British Labour Leader, said on his return from the interview which Hitler granted him. "If only I had been able to speak to him in German or he to me in English, I am sure we should have got on farther with each other!"

If you can't talk with a stranger who may be suspicious of you and who has come to see you, then the next best thing is to have an interpreter. Again the question arises, if we could get in touch with our Bees, might not our power to communicate with them— or at least their sense that we are 'communicable', sensible, rational, educationable creatures—possibly stand us in good stead? Could they not act as go-betweens between us and . . . ?

Well, we have to keep our minds open. And if our Bees here and now, our Bees which, like ourselves, are not nearly so old and advanced as insects could be in, say, a world whole geological ages ahead of ours; if our Bees have a form of rational communication quite unlike human speech, but still, like human speech, conveying ideas—then might not that prove of immense value to us? If we could get into touch with them here and now (and there seems no reason why we should not, as we have found out they have language and do notice in a rational way the things round them) then they might be able to act as invaluable translators and interpreters when, and if 'Bees' of a still more advanced breed might swarm upon us. Our Bees might help to bridge the gap between us and those 'others.' They could indicate to them that in spite of our unprepossessing appearance, our lack of method and order, our laziness-shot-with-violence, that we are not really or wholly creatures of blind instinct, but capable, if treated kindly, and not frightened into panic, not only of reasonable behaviour and of seeing things from our own interest and security, but also of something approaching at times to detached curiosity, and even, it is to be believed, of compassionate interest! "A truce to your fooling and insane speculation" cries the traditional naturalist, "Go back to the Bees!"

"Bees *are* creatures of instinct!" the traditional entomologist calls back. So much of their pattern, indeed all of it save this queer little anomalous behaviour, is obviously unconscious. Well, allow that you can tell whether someone who is doing something is conscious or not, by just watching him (a hard thing to prove). Does being able to do a thing 'automatically' mean that you cannot be conscious too, and at the same time? Not a bit of it. We know that when skill is very high, that is precisely what does happen. A skilled pianist will go on playing beautifully while, looking over his shoulder, he talks to you about something else. Perfect 'automatic processes' are in fact a help to the creative and most intelligent sides of the mind. Chopin said "My left hand carries on giving me the sound support I need, while with my right I feel my way out into new harmonies and airs."

So we can say that the following things are clear about Bees. They have built up their amazing economy over millions of years—there is evidence of plan and design. But it is fossilised, say the Instinctivists. It has certainly reached a marvellous perfection. But because it is that, and 'runs itself', as we say of a perfectly planned business, that does not mean that the Bees' mind has stopped thinking. It has no longer to think while it goes about the ordinary perfectly fixed and finished and efficient traffic of the hive—as a *corps de ballet* dancing a piece they have perfectly mastered, do not have to think but let their co-ordinated bodies weave the beautiful pattern. But that does not mean that the dancers have become puppets. They can speak to each other, and make comments on the audience and the orchestra and on one another, all the time their automatic system carries out the movements that they have taught it.

If we did not have an automatic system of perfect efficiency we should die. Fancy trying to keep heart beating, lungs breathing, the supply of oxygen and carbon dioxide right in the lung, the hydrochloric acid right in the stomach—not to speak of maintaining all the endocrine secretions in constant play. We should be dead in a few minutes; and during those few minutes, in our desperate struggle to keep alive, we should be distracted beyond all understanding, blindly absorbed in the mere internal effort to keep the machine from breaking down.

So automatism, instead of being contrary to intelligence, is the necessary aid and supporter of any freedom to understand and con-sider the outer world. We need not, we cannot and must not assume that Bees had their language from the beginning. It must have sprung up as ours did from the pressing needs of a close community life which also involved making long co-ordinated journeys outside the hive city. Maps, charts, logs and all the gear of exploration grow as men have to find their ways into unknown countries and open routes to bring back distant products.

Now if the mentality of our Bees has developed, why should not insects in the world of Mars—so much more ancient than ours—

116

have gone ahead? We should indeed assume that this must be so. Maybe they have had a world all to themselves. Certainly they have had geological time-spans more than the Bees here have enjoyed. But it may be said: They have only mosses and lichens —moss for breakfast, lichen for lunch, perhaps dried centipede for supper. But strange vegetables may have flowers as strange and wonderful as those extreme desert adaptations, the succulents, actually have. The succulents have succeeded in living in arid regions where heat and lack of water make a veritable Mars—and keen cold at night would make many plants wilt for good. The Bees have triumphantly specialised their diet even here, on our still lagging planet, so that they live entirely on the pure energy of sugar strengthened with some vitamins from the flowers.

On Mars they may have released sugar, as we are already hoping to do, by making a synthetic substance that will do, with water, air and sunlight, what chlorophyll now does, making the basic food, sugar, and of course able to make, if required, starch too. As to the lack of abundant water—small creatures would not need our supplies: there may be plenty underground on Mars: and the bee-masters of the planet may have learnt, what we are soon hoping to learn, and the eucalyptus tree has learnt already—to get all the water it needs by condensing moist air and making the drops run down into the ground.

We must add further to what has been glanced at above. We have seen that Bees have amazing eyes as well as wonderful power of scent, and probably fine hearing. Their sense-equipment is better than ours, as their energy, size for size, is much greater. Their eyes alone are a wonder. For not only can they see polarised light and the polarised markings made by such light—they can also see by ultra-violet light. They can see up into wavelengths to which our less effective eyes are blind. It has been found that they can respond to many flowers that seem to us dull and unnoticeable. Seen by ultra-violet light these blossoms are striking.

Their eyes surpass ours in another respect. As dusk comes on, though we can apply an ancient form of sight—'night-sight'— when we use it, it not only is dim, but even when the sky is only dusk all objects appear to us colourless, drained of all tint. All cats are not only grey in the dark—as the French maxim says: they are grey considerably before. That is not so with the Bees. As long as they can recognise an object at all, as long as there is any light at all, they see it coloured as truly as we perceive it in full light. When we think of those eyes we begin to wonder whether those upper air-cruisers with their baleful glare would really inconvenience a bee-pilot as severely as it would us poor weak-eyed humans?

One further argument must be met. It runs: You said that bees are limited in their size, and even on Mars (where things that are smaller may count for more because the pull of gravity is so much less than with us), how could such tiny creatures have built a fleet of space-ships and brought them across—when one of them may be 1,000 feet across! Of course Termites build cities that are sometimes as high as a small house. But when we think of whether a space-ship could be built by a super-bee we must remember two things. First they are immensely ahead of the Bees here—or any insect. And when we study the hive, even at its level with us, it is an amazing piece of skill. Since Bees have speech, they may soon turn to use other materials for the hive structure, instead of wax, though the original plan may be so good that it will not be changed much.

The second thing we must not forget is that skill can reduce force. The formula, "The more skill the less force", probably stands through every problem of manipulation.

If people of a superior mind and station had watched us in the Roman epoch; and right down to a hundred and twenty years ago, they would have said, "What pathetically and admirably industrious little creatures they are—but how slow and helpless they are in really tackling their environment. It is far too tough for such pygmies".

Then came steam, and then oil; and now bulldozers cut out roads that gangs of slaves could never have made in a hundredfold the time; and dynamite, like Thor with his hammer, shatters the rock that stands in our way.

What will we not be doing with our present atom power—if we

do not first use it on ourselves? "The more skill, the less force",
however, means even more than that. When you have real force
you do not have to unleash any kind of violence. Real skill means
that force is exerted without explosion. Look at what even we
have discovered about that essential power-process, the tempering
of steel, so as to give us our super-cutting tools.

Once, tempering steel in the mass was a scene out of the Inferno.
The blaze of the furnace scorched any flesh left bare and gave
cataract to eyes that dared to look into it. There was the hammer-
ing on giant anvils with bursts of sparks; the sudden explosive
quenching as the incandescent bar was plunged into water or oil.
Much, if not all of that, has been altered; for much tempering can
be done with absolute quiet, with no sense that it is going on, by
putting the bar between powerful magnets. It was rearrangement
of the atoms that gave steel its new temper. The magnet will do
that more exactly and with perfect quiet. Skill does away with
force. When we think what our electrical and magnetic knowledge
of metals will be in even another generation, would we not expect
intelligent life, geological ages ahead of us, to have made inventions, where, in as great a quiet as sugar or alcohol distills or water
condenses out of air, metals, far harder and more resilient and
lighter too than any we now know, would build themselves up
between the poles of some 'precipitating engine' in the very shape
that was desired, as a crystal is formed in a super-saturated solution.

We are experimenting today with a new type of engine, a power-
producer a dynamo of sorts, which could produce and employ in
serviceable amounts the small electric discharge which has been
found to be released every time that plates of a certain structure
are bent (the shifting of the atoms on the surface make a current).

But to do this—that is to say to get electric power in appreciable
amounts—we must have super-crystals of a certain size and a certain perfect form. Crystals of this perfection and dimension
Nature (always tending to work free-hand and sketchily) does not
produce—as far as we have been able to discover. So (for this
project was considered sufficiently worth while) intense research,
after many trials, has now begun to produce artificially these giant

and flawless crystals.* And this has been done by making a most ingenious 'field-machine'—or super-saturation pressure vessel. In this the crystals, if they are started at minute size—'seed' size— build themselves up. This, no doubt, is a first step toward a new and 'violenceless' way of producing, building up the parts and the gear we need for original departures in the plan and design of new power plant. We may soon be growing our engines instead of forging them.

So we need not bring their physical weakness against a set of super-bees, provided that their knowledge has, in the Baconian phrase, been turned by them into power. And there is a rumour that we may have some little proof on this very one point. That mysterious dispute as to the 'slag' on Maury Island beach? There is a rumour that it was not volcanic. That one piece did not, when tested, show that it was any ore yet known. Yet, it is said to have had in it elements that are known on earth—titanium and calcium among them. But—and this was the odd and significant suggestion —the calcium was in such amounts that, though it made a wonderfully heat-resisting alloy, it was not one we have yet managed to forge. It would be a wonderful stuff, for instance for the nozzles of super-jets—for that nozzle business is always a headache to power-designers. For long we have been able to make flames generate heats that were very high. The problem has been to find anything that would hold them, any duct that would not melt, even burn like a candle, once the attempt was made to lead the flame in the direction desired. We may learn much about metallurgy alone when we are allowed to examine at our leisure and with a competent guide—we will hope its pilot—a disc at rest.

But of course the best Bee point, in this case for their being the Lords of Mars and the masters of space-ships, lies in the queer mystery which so puzzled Commander MacLaughlin, the riddle of the "Gs." Granted, as he maintained, that the discs are 'manned'

* Note: Piezo-electricity (i.e. releasing electric current by bending quartz crystals, making them vibrate) has now given rise to two remarkable advances in power mechanism:— The required giant quartz crystals, eight inches long, are made up from 'seed' crystals that feed themselves on a nutrient medium made of crumbled quartz. (ii) The engine, powered by these vibrated crystals can yield 2000 volts at 75 amperes.

(and, even if there were doubts about the two-foot diameter saucers, there can be little doubt about the 'manning' of the big ones— 100 feet across) — and these large ones make the same amazing acceleration—then no creature larger than a large insect could stand that punch or kick.

This fact, when we combine it with the new evidence which we have just reviewed (the evidence that even the Bees have now attained to sign-speech and the drawing of maps), makes it difficult to resist the conclusion that Mars is ruled by insects. We recall that astronomers have said that if there is mobile life on Mars it would be insect in form.

The super sky-fleet that has now hung far above us for some three years, has also shown by its manoeuvring that it could be 'manned' only by crews with the resistance to pressure which an insect possesses. It is not only smallness which gives an insect immunity from crushing force exerted on a body accelerated in any gravitational field. The strength of an insect body is much greater than ours. Its structure is amazingly tough. We are so much soft tissue wrapped round slight rods made of lime. The insect keeps the soft paste, which makes its interior, shut up in curved cases made of the strange wonderfully tough material we call chitin. This carapace armour will, we know, considering its lightness, stand extraordinary pressures. Possibly the possession of this kind of frame might permit a Martian to emerge into this world.

Certainly, if the Martians are of such form as the rest of us (a soft body wound round a skeleton of light structure), then they could never hope to set foot here. They could cruise about in their discs. But, as we, if on the moon, would have to wear all-over armour (to protect ourselves from lack of air, cold and heat) so the Martians here would have to wear closely locked coats-of-mail, because the weight of the Earth's atmosphere at ground level is 15 pounds of pressure to the square inch. While it is generally agreed that on Mars the pressure is only $2\frac{1}{2}$ pounds.

Another factor which would make a manling from Mars helpless on our Earth would be the gravitational pull. Here, he, a creature evolved to stand up against the drag of a mass which is only some 4,200 miles in diameter, would have on this Earth to endure the down-drag of a sphere nearly 8,000 miles in diameter. On Jupiter, could we ever reach it and make a landing, we should have to crawl flat. To raise ourselves on our elbows might well be beyond our powers, so close would the giant planet's mass hold us to its breast.

A Martian of any kind, of human, mammal or indeed of any build but that of an insect, would be in much the situation on this Earth as we would be in on Jupiter. But, if he or it were an insect, he or it would have the intense strength which insects show here. Their flight alone, their wing power, is the release of an energy which an elephant might envy. Their four-wing 'vortex flight' is real flight, not the clumsy skidding and flapping on the air which is all the birds can do, and which we somewhat more clumsily imitate. Indeed their wonderful natural flight may have been what first turned the rulers of the Martian insect world to think of artificial flight, as we know the flight of birds gave man the inspiration to follow them into the air.

Chapter XII

WERE THEY PREPARING?

BUT, it will be said, if the Martian insects were getting ready to visit us, might we not have detected the first signs that they were preparing to make a descent? Has not Mars been watched as none other of our fellow planets? It has always been the one which was most observable and which, because its surface is so naked of cloud, gave us most points of interest to consider. We know this is true. No other star has raised the temperature of astronomers so high or made them flush so fiercely.

The whole surface of the planet has been mapped with wonderful care—in spite of the difficulties presented in watching it. The canal controversy has been mentioned above, and everyone has views about Martian engineering.

It will and should be asked, "When the canals were being detected, why did no one discover the preliminary plans for the larger venture? This descent could not have been planned in a moment. We should have been able to detect the first tentative pushings out, the launching stations. Why didn't we?"

The answer, strange to say, seems to lie in the fact that we didn't know what to look for; so that when we found it, we didn't know what to make of it. For, quite early we did discover something about Mars that was harder to explain than the canals. For the strangest thing about Planet Four is not something on it but two things about it.

In August 1877 Mars made one of its 'nearest to the earth' approaches. Every fifteen to seventeen years — particularly in August—Mars and ourselves are nearest. The last very good time was 1941. The next very good time will then be about 1956, (though there will be a fairly good date in 1952 when the 200 inch telescope will try for some photographs).

When in August 1877 Mars had come close, Asaph Hall of the

Naval Observatory at Washington (D.C.) trained the 26 inch telescope on it. On the night of the 11th August he made his first great discovery. At first he could not be sure. Then he was certain—there was a minute body racing round above the surface of Mars—Mars had a satellite, a moon. On the 17th he had found another and it was even closer to the Martian surface. The two were amazingly small. Indeed they cannot be properly seen.

We see them, as we see motes in sunlight, things too small to be seen in themselves, but noticeable by the flash that the sunbeam strikes off as it touches them. So in spite of all attempts to gauge their size we cannot certainly say what it is. If they are of a dull texture, the smaller—which is the outer and has been christened Deimos—may be ten miles in diameter and the inner (called Phobos) a little larger. But that measurement depends on taking for granted that these objects are pills of globular rock—moons cast out of Mars, as our moon is supposed to have been cast out of Earth—a theory which in any case has many critics.

This old-fashioned theory would say then that these two midget 'moons' would be of the same shade as their mother Mars. But, of course, if these two satellites were composed of a brighter substance than ordinary Martian earth, they would be much smaller. For the flash they give—by which their size is gauged—could come more brightly from a far smaller body, if that body were for instance a gleaming globe or disc.

Though the astronomers of pre-air-war were not prepared to speculate or even to imagine man making a synthetic satellite to circle our Earth, they were puzzled to explain these anomalous 'moons'. Phobos, the inner—which incidentally flashes the more brightly—is so near the surface of the planet that it has to go at an immense pace to keep from crashing (speed, by raising centrifugal force, counteracts the centripetal drag of gravitation). Its speed is such that it gets round its mother planet in one third of a Martian day-and-night (diurnal rotation). This of course must have a strange effect for those looking up at it. To relieve the monotony of the whole heavenly host rising in the east and setting in the west, this small intimate 'moon' rises in the west and sets in the east. It gets round Mars twice while Mars rotates once.

The other midget moon behaves in an opposite way. Deimos, which is some distance farther out from the surface of Mars, seems as tardy as its lower companion Phobos is hasty. Deimos's period is only six days greater than the Martian day. So, to those looking up at it, it appears to go so slowly that it takes two days between rising and setting.

What was anyone to make of such anomalies? The astronomers of pre-rocket days did their best. They speculated mildly. They did suggest that these odd companions might not be specks of eruptive Martian matter that the planet once spewed out. Then what? Well, they might be captured Asteroids. We have already mentioned the Asteroid belt lying beyond Mars on the way to Jupiter. It may have a very serious part to play in this Disc Drama.

The capture of a stray Asteroid by a planet is not an impossibility. When in 1932 what is now called Anteros (and then was named the Reinmuth Object) in its plunging through space came within twenty minutes of the earth, we might well have found ourselves with a midget moon, if indeed it had not made a direct hit, when we would possibly have been worse off than if we had set off the Hydrogen Bomb. (By the way, those who think that we are hopelessly panicky should take comfort by reflecting that although this small star was within twenty minutes of ramming us —with inconceivable results—no one showed anything but the faintest curiosity in the encounter. The writer knows, for he was making the commentary on current science in London for the radio then). But Anteros went off and has not made a lunge at us since. So the capture of Asteroids and their becoming sham satellites seems too rare.

As far as we know, as far as our eyes tell us, Asteroids, meteorites from the Asteroid belt, are always drifting in toward the Sun, in from their orbit, as leaves fall in autumn. We see only those that graze through our torpedo-net of the atmosphere and are there caught and burn themselves up into harmless dust through the friction. Mars has a much smaller gravitation field than we have to attract such visitors. Hence it would have less chance of being molested. If we have escaped, Mars has a better chance of escaping.

The surface of Mars seems innocent of scars when we think of our own surface and that of the pockmarked moon, our satellite. Mars seems to have cooled before volcanic eruptions took place. Lowell thought that it had only one low range of mountains reaching the very moderate height of 3,000 feet, the Mountains of Mitchell near its southern pole. Had Mars been often hit—as many of the vast craters on the moon are now thought to be 'bullet marks' made by meteorites that have struck full force on the moon-surface (unscreened by an atmosphere)—then on the Martian landscape we should have seen these great rampart rings —some on the moon are thirty miles across and throw most striking shadows. But not a trace of such has been detected on Mars.

When, therefore, Dr. Walter Haas, Director of the Association of Lunar and Planetary Observers and Mathematics Instructor at the University of New Mexico, reported that a Japanese Fellow of the Association had sent in a report of an Explosion on Mars on 15th January 1950 powerful enough to have been observed through the eight-inch reflector at the Osaka City Planetarium, Dr. Hass's explanation, that the explosion was probably of volcanic nature, does not seem borne out by the nature of the planet. If it has never had volcanoes before, why should it start having them now?

But if at last intelligent life is making a great effort to command sufficient power to take a decisive part in Planetary Politics, then we might expect that a cloud of dust 60 miles high and billowing out for nearly one thousand miles, might mark another milestone in the Martian progress in releasing energy. We must only hope that this progress has not brought dangerously near that limit of planetary stress and power of cohesion which was passed by the planet that once was Mars' outer neighbour and now is so much space-flotsam.

The theory that these two very odd satellites of Mars are asteroids, captured meteors, is not very strong. But some theory is needed to account for them. They are anomalous. But no other theory was possible for respectable astronomers, before the almost insane inventive power of engineers began to show the sky-men what could be run up into the sky; and, further, began to calculate how you might not only pierce the space beyond the atmosphere, but actually make fixtures yourself in the empty vault of space.

We have seen that we do now definitely plan, as our first step out into space, and as a springboard to launch us to the moon and so on to Mars, to make a synthetic satellite—one 500 miles out and then another, a still farther-out jetty to lie or ride on a still farther orbit. We say it is possible and will be the way to launch space-ships. (We also plan that our synthetic satellite shall circle our planet in two hours! Phobos must look to his speed-laurels!)

Very well. Would not a people ahead of us do precisely the same thing? If what now actually rides above us (a space fleet with a mother-ship of great size) came from Mars, then we should expect to sight, just off the surface of Mars and speeding round it, the two similar launching jetties of the type which we intend to place round ourselves.

In the super-disc soaring round us, say 500 miles high, we have this end of the arch of thrown traffic which has its bases the two so-called 'moons' of Mars, Phobos and Deimos. We have accounted for the anomaly they present, and we have found the very proof that we were rightly asked to provide. If they have come here then surely there should be proof and sign of their preparation, preparation which would have actualised and fulfilled the counter-plans—the plans for our space voyage—which we have already made. We should be able to sight their home-base ships from which they launch their Mars-to-Earth flights. We have!

As a postscript to this Chapter we may add one other possible objection to space-flight (and so to space-visitors). It has been raised; and the answer to it, as a matter of fact, may rather confirm than weaken the hypothesis that our visitors have by now arrived safely, and are waiting out beyond our farthest atmospheric doorstep, outside our extremest 'territorial airs' frontier.

It is known from the routine reports of upper atmosphere exploration by the rocket launchings at the White Sands (New Mexico) base, that, possibly, one of these great record-carrying rockets did not return. It may not have crashed at any spot at present known. It is unlikely that it fell back on United States territory. Just possibly it plunged into some part of the vast

Pacific. But there is a rumour that the theodolite team, tracking it, had it in view until suddenly it vanished.

This might imply three possible things :—

(i) That it penetrated some blue layer of high sky, some outer atmospheric stratum which (at that hour at least) was impenetrable to our sight. Because we can see the stars at night, that does not mean we can see them by daylight and we all know how wraith-like even the moon looks when the sun is up. This rocket may not either then have vanished but gone on up or down.

(ii) Could it have gone on and up, shaken off the grip of our world and become an asteroid on its own, a midget planet, a free meteorite? There is reason however to presume that it was not going at 20,000 miles per hour which is the speed calculated as necessary for a rocket if it is to free itself from the down-pull of the Earth's gravitational field and escape into space. If then it did not escape or crash on some unobserved part of our globe—if indeed it vanished because, as the observers watched, it actually dissolved, what could have caused that sudden destruction?

(iii) It may have run into something. Here again there are three possibilities, three possible obstacles it may have struck:

(a) It was hit by a meteor which at that almost airless level was neither pulverised nor checked by atmospheric friction. But experts on meteors think that the sky is not thickly sown with them. And if they are fragments from the asteroid belt and/or the solid spray of a comet's tail, they cannot be so common in a space as vast as the solar system.

(b) The rocket blew up, burnt in a moment to dust, because it ran into such heat that it was pulverised. Now we have to face up to the odd fact that it is not true to say (as we had for long assumed) "the higher the colder". The highest atmosphere (and possibly outer space) may be said to be hot, quite as logically as it may be said to be cold. How? Heat is caused by the swift motion of molecules. They move very rapidly at the top of the atmosphere. Hence it must be hot. But, on the other hand, though these molecules move very fast, there are very few of them. Which would make you feel warmer—a mild hot-water pipe-system round your room, or a dozen oxyacetylene torches dashing about, but hundreds of yards distant? So neither (a) meteoric knock-out nor (b) high-atmosphere heat-incineration could account for a massive rocket's disappearance. There remains only:

(c) The rocket was hit intentionally. And if an artificial satellite has been "planted" in our circumference: if the crew of this space-ship saw rushing up toward their orbit this dreadful derelict torpedo: if they knew (from their White Sands intimate study of such a rocket on its way upward) that it was "unmanned" and "flying blind"—they would of course shoot at it, to get it out of their path. For they might well think, "This is the first trial at making an artificial satellite on the part of the Earth creatures. And if this object can establish itself on the orbit we have now chosen and taken, it will be a constant collision-danger to us on our routine traffic lane".

So the masters of a space-ship "riding under our lee" must argue and act. And if it is claimed (as it is) that the Nazis' "Artificial Satellite Project" was to launch such an orbital ultra-atmosphere ship, and that ship was to destroy our cities with heat rays (generated from the unscreened sun) then the present launchers and masters of the satellite space-ship would have a ray which could vaporise the errant rocket. Its sudden disappearance would then tell not against space-travel and space-shipping in our offing, but in favour of such a theory.

I

Chapter XIII
WHY NOW?

"WHY NOW?" is the next question. *Have* they made the springers for their space-bridge? *Have* they 'floating jetties' riding at gravitation-anchor off their own bow (we do not know how long they have had them; we saw them first in 1877, but if Martians are as much ahead of us, as their planet is more advanced in its development for dry-land life, then they may have been out sailing in their synthetic satellites millions of years ago).

If we whose earth is still more than three-fifths water-covered and who have climbed into the air in power-craft only during the past fifty years, if we now have rockets that have gone 250 miles above this earth's surface (the 'two-stage' V-2 WAC Corporal rocket—the V-2 giving the kick for the first part of the flight and then falling off; the WAC Corporal then, having reached the really thin air, being able to make, at the highest speed yet known, the second part of the climb)—if we have to face such a conclusion, at least we can make one objection to the whole thing:— Granted they could have come long before, why in the name of Space and Solids did they not come before? Would *we* have waited? You bet we would not.

But that argument is not conclusive. Indeed there is an old motto that suggests why Martian insect-brains may have thought and thought again before taking the plunge. "Fools rush in where angels fear to tread".

Then why do they come *now*? If you are an angel, a sceptic once remarked, it is easy to abstain from rushing in, because you do not have to tread, you fly. They have flown, and even now they do not alight. Are we sure they do not inspect us every so often—are we sure that they have not been paying periodic visits just to give us a look over? We have no such negatively reassuring certainty. Indeed we have a considerable amount of positive evidence, if

130

evidence means anything, and is not crushed flat under the slam of the retort "Incredible". We have a considerable amount of evidence which we need no longer dismiss as nonsense, now that we know that high-sky riding is possible, and, more—that more beings may be at the game than ourselves.

For years a patient student of science worked painstakingly through the special papers of the various learned societies. He could have been a professor with the amount of knowledge that he collected—had he wished not to find facts but to support current theories. But he did wish to find out as many odd facts as he could, he did not want to link them up with each other or with any orthodox theory, religious or scientific. Emphatically he did not want to support the professional scientist; and it amused rather than shocked him, when he found that facts contradicted the text-book. He did not like hypotheses — after all Sir Isaac Newton felt the same! *Hypotheses non fingo!*—"I don't touch hypotheses". He strongly objected to hypotheses being dressed up and called Natural Laws.

This student, Charles Fort by name, finally collected enough material of 'Anomalia' to fill four large volumes—the main stuff can now be had in one. Part of his great study deals with strange 'air-ships' viewed before man had any. The subject is so extensive that there is not room here to spread it out in its amplitude. Briefly then, there are references going back to the eighteenth century. During the nineteenth they continue and become more numerous. By the last quarter of the past century they are frequent.

Twice in 1870—the year, incidentally of the Franco-Prussian war, when it was clear that Germany would bid for world power —sky-ships were seen.

On 1st August 1870, high above the Riviera and seeming to move slowly, there passed a globular body that must have been of great size. The September before, on the twenty-sixth of the month, something was seen high up at night, an elliptical body that, for half a minute, was watched crossing the moon's face. It seemed to have some kind of fan at its stern, or a rudder. This recalls the object seen by the watchers at Idyllwild on the 22nd March 1950.

Nature reported in 1880 the bright luminous globes moving high

131

up in the sky which are still observed. (The latest report on 2nd August 1950 is from San Rafael, all the way south along the Pacific Coast down to the San Francisco peninsula).

A writer in the *Bermuda Royal Gazette* in 1885 saw an unidentifiable 'thing' high in the skies over the West Indian islands.

Then, in the same year, Adrianople in European Turkey was visited or looked down upon by a 'disc'. The observers gauged its size from that of the moon. Though the object was sailing high it looked several times larger than the disc of the moon.

New Zealand had a fast moving oval to report from its sky in 1888.

In the early 'nineties the Dutch East Indies were inspected—in this case by what seem to have been cones—a pattern that may now have been discarded, though one or two present day references seem to show that a triangular craft has been sighted over America during the present visits.

On they go, like the drip of a tap, like the slow gathering of a drop. Every couple of years or so they are sighted. A disc with a rudder or fan was reported by a British battleship in 1894; and in 1895 triangular high-sky objects were seen by many in England and Scotland: and, of course, dismissed as 'illusion by officials and experts—who had not seen them!

Then was the turn of the United States of America to begin to get more than its share of the high-sky limelight. The year of the Victoria Diamond Jubilee gave a number of the United States a sky-show. Beginning in the second week in April the 'ship' made a tour of the Middle West. It was watched through telescopes by students of astronomy. From their accounts, the object, cigar-shaped with short wings at the side, may have been the 'tube model' in one of its earlier forms, the tube model that has given such remarkable demonstrations of its performance to air pilots. The 'tube' too, as we know from those today, emitted strange lights. In this case they flickered much and ranged in colour—as have some of the lights we now witness—but in these late cases they seem not to be attached to any visible craft.

In this 1897 case the coloured beams wove such patterns and ranged from red to white and on to green; so that it was thought that the ship was signalling. No one succeeded in making a contact. The ship moved to the Atlantic States and the Virginia town of Sisterville was roused to see that it was being scanned by searchlights that wandered over the countryside—seeking what? The red and green lights showed along the sides of the ship which seemed 200 feet long and had small flukes at its sides.

A cigar model in the summer of 1907 sailed over Vermont; and after it was gone an explosion took place in the sky. But when a year later Massachusetts was visited by a similar craft, it played only with its searchlights.

In 1910, on a January morning, the cigar appeared silver. It cruised about over the State of Alabama. In 1912 *Popular Astronomy* carried a careful report of a black object crossing the face of the moon.

There were not many reports after that. West Virginia had a visit in 1919; but the inhabitants thinking that it was dirigible from some home base, felt no disquietude. When it was later reported that no home or earth-foreign dirigible was then aloft, people by that time had begun to think of something else.

There is evidence, however, that when World War II started, uninvited visitors were looking on. Were the Allies' flying officers always deluded when they thought that sometimes they were tracked and even accompanied by small, fast-flying little discs or globes ('foo planes' they called them) that paced them? Certainly after the war most of us saw notices copied from the Swedish newspapers of strange fiery vehicles that swept across the Swedish sky. But knowing Sweden's position and proximity most people were certain this could have only one explanation. These references did not all come from Sweden—they spread, until in most months or even weeks you could pick up a reference to some sighting through Europe and even in North Africa.

Then America came into her own. As the foremost flying country she had a right to early information—and, possibly, inspection. A great year was 1947—perhaps *the* great year. But June, though it launched a keen interest that even now cannot be quite discounted, was not the month of the appearance of the new crop, the new flush of sightings.

133

They began to blossom in April, and the first was a theodolite sighting. The user of the theodolite was tracking a weather balloon. It happens to be the first case in the file of sightings which Project Saucer released when it dissolved. But the comments of the sighter are not given. So we cannot rate this theodolite record with the other two, Mr. Hall of Emmet, Idaho and Commander MacLaughlin of White Sands, New Mexico.

May yielded two saucers, one from Oklahoma and another from Colorado. So we note one thing: these visitors have been seen before. We may add another, that they first paid more attention to Europe and then increasing attention to the United States of America.

We may close with an obvious deduction :— That they were first interested in Europe because a generation ago it was still leading industrially; they are now more interested in the United States of America because it leads the world in industrial production. We may perhaps add a rider; these visitors may be coming at certain times (as well as hovering over certain countries) because they fear what our industrialisation seems to lead to—intensive wars that drive us finally to the air, to rockets, to atom power, to the capacity not only to destroy ourselves, but to make into a kind of cosmic bomb "the great globe itself, yea all which it inherit".

We see then that the visitors have been coming before—how long before, no one can say. They do not seem to have the slightest intention of interfering with us, provided we do not interfere with them, either by invading their territory or by upsetting the apple-cart of the solar system on which they depend as much as ourselves. We have seen that they have good reason for looking far more often and far more carefully than previously, now that we are up to really big mischief. Why are they coming in such numbers now, no longer as "single spies but in battalions"? Because we are a peril to them, seems the only sensible answer.

But are we, can we be a peril to them? It will not be generations before we think in schedule terms of going to the moon. They will have warning enough and time enough when they see us launch our first synthetic satellite. But the danger might be much nearer and much more emphatic than that. A bad boy with matches, out in a barn that not only adjoins your house but is full of hay, is a far more immediate peril than a burglar who is loitering half a mile away on the other side of a boatless river, looking with idle covetousness at your distant windows.

Seriously we must ask, "Are we a peril to them? Is there anything in their past history to make them suspicious of their neighbours and of the harm a disaster to a neighbour may do to them?"

We are all, on our planets, like men on small craft in a big ocean. We ride the tide but we have to be seaworthy to do so. The precise balance and poise of a planet, as it rides its orbit, spins on its axis, and rocks on its poles—so giving years and seasons and days and nights, all as necessary to life as is air is to a man floating on the sea—that balance and poise is as delicate as that of a ship. We find it hard to believe that. But it is true.

There is some evidence that the Poles of our earth shift fairly easily. We know that the Magnetic Pole is always rocking and that the 'third motion of the earth' is its waltz on its axis. There is, too, some evidence from geology and paleobotany that would seem to show that the earth's Poles may have shifted considerably in the past and in the not very remote past.

The coal measures at the Poles may be ascribed to the fact that when they were being laid down the whole planet was hot and steamy under a white thick coverlet. But when we find their fossils in what are now Arctic rocks we begin to wonder. Further, when we find remains of the grape vine in Lapland it suggests a considerable change of climate and the former existence of a warm if not hot North Pole. South African geologists point out that nearly all the 'erratics', the boulders of alien strata, often of immense size, that were carried across countrysides by the glaciers of the Ice Ages, all seem to have streamed not up from the south, but to have come down in a north-westerly direction, from what is now the equatorial Atlantic. This seems to point to a shift of the Poles.

Were that so, could we tip our axis by firing off a bomb? It is a risk. For when the deep-sea firing of an Atom Bomb was suggested, as part of the Bikini exploit, a Yale Professor Emeritus of Chemistry wrote begging that it should not be done. He felt that it was clear to all geophysicists that if an Atom Bomb were exploded in the depths of the Pacific Ocean close to the Equator this would give a maximum provocation to the earth to 'heel over'. For the weight of water that lies in the world, is such that if it were suddenly raised or partly lifted, the ocean floor, already (or at the same time) having been given a tremendous blow, might buckle.

We know that when so small an engineering undertaking as the cutting of the Culebra Channel of the Panama Canal was being carried out, accompanied by the removal of large masses of earth, the exposed lower layers which were to be the floor of the canal actually rose—to the surprise of the engineers. When the weight had been lifted from them, they buckled: the so-called crust of the earth is a much more springy and balanced thing than we have supposed.

We often talk of the Balance of Nature. By that we generally mean the adjustment of one species against another; so, for example, if there are many birds, the insect population can be kept within proportions; but if many cats are introduced, the insects will increase. Evidently, with the super-engineering we now employ, when above all (or perhaps one should say 'below all') we start rousing up the basic energy of all matter and loose atomic power, we must take care.

The solid earth is not at all so solid. Long before we start vaporising it we have to warn ourselves that the firm earth is not at all firm—it spins. So if the bomb at Bikini had been made a depth bomb and had lifted that mass of water (as well it might, turning vast volumes straight from water to steam) then up the floor of the ocean might have come (let alone the superheated 'magma' from under the lithosphere—the rind of rock that insulates us from the infernal heats). Then this sudden bulge on our belt—this rotational rupture—could have sent us on to another spin, another slant. Whether this scientific adviser was right or not, we may never know. But that his advice was sufficiently weighty we may judge. For although the surface blast was proceeded with, the depth Atom Bomb was never fired. The project was abandoned.

Now since the point at issue at the moment is not our convenience but the inconvenience we might cause Mars, even if we tipped
ourselves up and so ruined the world-climate for good, would that
gravely perturb the Martians? Evidently planets can get their
poles pointing straight at the Sun. Uranus has a moon that, as
far as can be judged, is in that position toward its mother planet
and it seems to go over the top of its mother planet. Some
astronomers have thought that perhaps Venus so spins in relation
to the Sun. (The white blanket that wraps Venus is so uniform that
it is hard to be sure how that globe is revolving). If so, it is a bad
outlook for the future life on Venus. For as soon as the cloud
lifts or breaks, then good-bye to any further development of biotics.
Because then one side will be baking like a furnace and the other
far colder than any refrigerator. Along the edge "where night
meets not dawn—but a white hell" there would be a tempest like
nothing on earth as the shreds of the torn atmosphere were rushed
and dragged from the space-zero cold to a heat which might well
disperse the air into space.

If that is so, Venus spinning on its side and not upright has
done us no harm. Nor is there any reason to suppose that, even
if that change of poise has taken place during the time that life
has existed on this planet of ours, the change has been at all
harmful to us. Why then should Mars be concerned because we
might reel over like a drunk man? We should still be spinning
round in our orbit, our original orbit round the sun—still a safe
50,000,000 miles or so from Mars' orbit-path.

There is however, another danger which really might inconvenience Martians. We might blow up. Dr. Jeffries, one of our most
eminent geophysicists, thinks that all planets may suffer from
internal strains, tidal stresses in their cores. He believes that the
moon may yet blow up and present us first with some splendid
rings, such as Saturn alone has worn till now, and then the moon
fragments would fall from this belt and make a real belt, a huge
mountain range, of debris all round our equator.

The earth's rind of rock (called the lithosphere) as mentioned
above, may not be at all thick. It may be possible with the explos-

ive powers of the modern atom to burst through it. Then, quite likely, out would come our molten insides.

The famous eruption of Krakatoa, in the Dutch East Indies, gave a relatively small but awesomely impressive demonstration of what that sort of pyrotechnic display might be. There part of an island, which was volcanic, blew itself into the ocean and the Pacific took up the challenge. For some time internal heat and the vast ocean had some exciting rallies. But before the dispute spread, a patched-up peace was somehow made. If however the gap had been large enough there seems little reason why the dispute should have terminated, so long as there was fire not put out by water and water yet to be vaporised by fire.

Perhaps one day, planet by planet, the whole solar system will explode. So far it has not done so. But is it true and demonstrable that no planet has as yet blown up? Certainly not. As long ago as the 'twenties the great Swedish astronomer, Dr. Ludblad, had introduced to the Astronomic world his theory of the Asteroids. He maintained that they were the wreckage and flotsam of two exploded planets. The theory met more and more of the problems that this welter of planet-fragments does arouse.

Now, in the first International Astronomic Conference held since the war, it was generally decided that there was a planet on an orbit now filled with rock-wreckage (some the size of islands—e.g. the asteroid called Ceres).

It has been called Asteroida. What sort of planet does it seem to have been? First of all it is estimated that its size was some-what about the size of Mars. Being out still farther from the Sun it would be as much 'further ahead' of Mars, as Mars is 'further ahead'—more advanced in its development—than we are. Secondly —and of this there is direct evidence, of a sort we have about no other star nor planet, of the geological structure of the Asteroids and therefore of Asteroida.

There are two sorts of stranded asteroids, two sorts of meteorites. As these fragments drift by on their way to the Sun, and are now and then captured by Earth's gravitational field, and, if not burnt to dust, fall on our surface, they are found to be of two types.

One is lithic—rock fragments, rock fragments that have been

found to contain all the minerals, all the elements that we have here and none other. There is also a persistent rumour that researchers have found bacteria in the hearts of these sky-stones, but this has never been confirmed, for the bacteria may have been introduced since the 'rocks' have been on this earth and indeed while they were being examined.

The other type of meteorite is metal, nickel iron. Now put those two facts together and conclusion is hardly escapable. For our earth is constructed in the same way—a rind of rock and a great heart of something that weighs exactly as if it were nickel iron.

So it seems clear that Asteroida was a planet like ours. And it blew up. Its explosion may well have marked a turning point in Martian life. It may have been a terrific sight: and on Mars, with so little atmosphere to screen it from cosmic missiles, life must for a time have resembled existence in a severe air-raid.

Sky suicide—a world committing *felo-de-se*—is no private matter. And if Earth exploded, it might be serious for Martians. The fragments of our big body would not fall on them; but turning ourselves into a dust belt, and filling our entire orbit with a thick mist of fragments, we might cut off a dangerously large amount of the sparse sunlight they now get. A cosmic cloud of fine dust particles, into which our solar system ran, is now perhaps the most tenable explanation of the last terrible ice age. Only let the temperature fall a few degrees, and we would have the ice back— and then good-bye to our present civilisation.

Maybe it was Asteroida's explosion that did produce enough dust to cause us to have our last paralysing glaciations. So Mars could not consider with complacence our fouling by even one per cent. the pellucidity of the solar system's sky. We and Mars are practically on the same plane, so that even a fine belt of dust made by our fragments would be capable of depriving Mars of its desperately needed sunlight.

There is a further and maybe a far graver risk that we with our ridiculously disproportionate powers (disproportionate to our self-control) are running for ourselves and for the Martians. The little belt of mist which we could create by pulverising ourselves and leaving our coil and ring of smoke neatly to cut off the Martian sunlight—that blanketing procedure might fail. We might disintegrate wholly or into such large fragments as not to form a belt of fog. And this is speculation for the future—perhaps clear deduction for the Martians, with their greater powers of calculation arising from their far advanced knowledge of the forces with which we are now monkeying. Moreover, what is not speculation but clear observation may have a far more perilous meaning.

Just at the very time that we chose to fire off our Atom Bombs —with considerable wantoness considering our abysmal ignorance of the consequences—no less important a body than the Sun itself chose to 'act up'. We know that the largest sunspots that have even been seen on the face of the Sun did appear just at that time. "Post hoc, ergo propter hoc" say the conservatives and reactionaries —"just chance association!"

We did this; and then, out there, that happened. We must remember we have no way of finding out the connection of events other than by making something happen and then watching all round to see if anything out of the common occurs in consequence. There is no denying that when we made use of our super-force, when we released for the first time atomic energy, then the Sun did do something we have never seen before. It did produce the biggest spots ever recorded—monster things.

Of course our puny efforts could never affect such a monster body. Into one of those spots you could put twenty of our worlds in a row, and then they might not quite stretch across it! Yet there is such a thing as 'trigger action' in the Universe. A catalyst in one part in a million, and indeed less, can set off a complete reaction. A virus not a couple of molecules across can explode a deadly disease that will reduce our bodies (monstrous in size compared to a virus) to a heap of decay.

Furthermore, when we study sunspots, the actual things, we find that they are profoundly queer and profoudly powerful 'centres'. They seem to be vortices, frantic storms that tear open the photosphere—the dazzling blaze of flame that is the Sun's outer 'skin'. And then out of these monstrous 'gun ports' there is shot intense short-wave radiation. They are whirlpools of short-radiation or, as we used to call it, the light that is beyond light. They are much more penetrating than ordinary visible light. They pierce our atmosphere; derange all our radio; cause, there can be little doubt, all sort of mutations in the genes, (the heredity-bearing units in living creatures); profoundly upset the weather; alter the crop yield; and, maybe, cause sudden rises of insanity and hysteria by attacking our nervous system. Sunspots are our Problem Number One in celestial forces.

But we could not be a provocative of such tempests! Are we sure? We do know that the pull of the planets does contribute towards one of the causes which approximately every eleven years brings about the periodic cycle of sunspot activity. We know also that they are magnetic fields.

Now the Earth is a very powerful magnetic field. Its huge heart of nickel iron—a heart perhaps huger, considering this globe's actual size, than that of most of the other planets—makes it a very powerful magnet and it is comparatively close to the Sun. Could it be a trigger-piece in the sunspot explosion rhythm?

Is there any evidence of this? Yes. Observations made in France in the 'twenties seemed to show what then appeared a highly anomalous fact—that as on the face of the Sun, as the Sun spins round, a sunspot comes so that it begins to face directly toward us, its shape often changes. This fact was noted as strange. But it would seem to suggest that we, though so small (even when we are not playing with Atom Power as a catalytic aid to cataclysm) do make the sunspots alter their behaviour.

Lastly, the Martians have a paramount reason for the strongest wish that we should not increase the short-wave radiation from the Sun. Astronomer after astronomer has pointed out that one of the reasons why it was hard to accept life on Mars, even vegetable life, was the fact that the Martian atmosphere was so thin that Martians had not enough protection from the short-wave rays from the Sun that are deadly to life—at least at the stage we know it—and these, in sufficient force, must make the high balance of the living cell and of the gene impossible, by breaking down that delicate relation.

There is however a far greater risk, far greater than just making the Sun sterilise all of us, and inflict 'X-ray Burns' that would kill us. We might—a few of us, some of us here and some of us on Mars—for in this matter we would all be of the same family—the family of life: and all in the same boat, the solar system being flooded with super-solar radiation—a scanty remnant of us, of all life from the two planets on which it has achieved emergence, might creep underground and escape. But there would be no escaping this second and far greater peril.

But could there be a greater peril? Yes. Just one more is more terrible. It too comes from the Sun. The Sun is in technical language a Cophoid—that is a pulsing star, one whose light and radiation and, indeed, probably its bulk, vary and fluctuate on some mysterious atomic tide. These stars which have been one of the first interests of astronomers, for they give a way of estimating the size of the Universe, when the usual method, the parallax, will no longer serve for measurement on such a scale—these pulsing stars have also, it is thought, another thing to tell us.

They may tell us about the nature of Atomic Force. They are supposed to lessen and swell because, in the fabulous pressures that go on inside a sun, the compression becomes so intense that at last all the electrons are stripped from the atom-core. Then the atom somehow "rebounds", re-gathers the electrons of which it has been robbed, and once again the star recovers its size. But what if it did not?

There is, it is supposed, another end to the story, rare but not infrequent. Instead of recovering, the star may explode. Novae, perhaps the most amazing phenomena of the whole night sky, seem to be stars that suddenly broke all their bounds. And the stars which are most likely to do that are precisely Cepheids. Further among Cepheids there seems to be one type which is most liable to explode. That is the type which is called from size and colour an Orange Dwarf.

Now the serious matter lies precisely here. Our Sun is not only a Cepheid; this has been allowed for some time. But there is no doubt that it is an Orange Dwarf. We long ago faced the fact that our glorious Sun was not really much of a sun. It does well enough for us, but in the monstrous scale of the Universe, its rank is not high. Only lately have we realised that though it was modest to look upon, its possibilities were dangerous. No one knows when a Cepheid will explode. It is one of the keenest hunts that is now going on in the sky—to see if there is any way of recognising a pre-nova, a star that is ready to burst. Does its spectrum show any shadows to forecast that blinding event? No one knows. What is suspected is that something quite hidden and perhaps catalytic may be the trigger that sets off this cosmic mine.

The sunspots may be warnings of digestive trouble—as spots on our own face sometimes tell about our interior conflicts. If so, the storm signals have been flying doubly flagged at the mast-head since we began to try to make earthspots with our bomb. Is it not possible that the Martians, who have so much to fear from sun-trouble, may have read these signs? Why should they not—so far ahead of us and so anxious about sunlight—have watched and studied our common luminary and life-giver, and know its fever-times, and watch with anxiety its possible epileptic seizures. On that ground alone, on the ground that the spots have been so big of late, they might have assumed that some trouble was brewing. And knowing that the pull of the planets is at least one cause of the spot-outbreak, they might have checked over the planets to see why their pull, their magnetic stresses, their ordinary atomic structures should have led to what is perhaps an unprecedented disturbance in the pivot of the whole system.

And then they would come to us. They would find the mischief lying at our door. Even if the sunspots had not raised the alarm, even if the Sun had not signalled in so unmistakable a way, they must have seen our fatal signal. When we twice struck Japan and then, not to slaughter, but to astound, made the Pacific spout—when we, time and again, sent up great super-thunderheads of smoke, spray and the wreckage of human industry and human bodies, right up into the stratosphere, then we put out a finger to beckon attention on any watching fellow-planet that we were out for trouble, and able to give it. They could hardly have failed to see that defiant, wanton signal. With the Sun showing major spots, with their knowledge of what those spots mean, with their knowledge of what is the dangerously-delicately-balanced nature of that

143

furnace of force we call our day-bringer, they could not have failed to conclude that the time for action had come.

We close for the moment the question 'Why Now?' It is we who have decided why now anyone who cares for the solar system should look in on us and ask us to be careful. When a Cepheid explodes it turns into a mass of flame which races out at speed that in a few weeks has transformed it from an insignificant star to one of the wonders of the sky. But only a wonder to someone fabulously far off. Near by, for any planetary body of such a sun, the display is a horror. In a matter of hours—during which the heat would rise to deadly heights—the flame itself would reach us and the earth would probably be vaporised as it was engulfed. It would probably extend out as far as the orbit of Mars, and though Mars might not be melted, all life upon it would vanish.

The star that has erupted shrinks again, and soon becomes, in many cases, smaller than it was before. It seems that it often shrinks till it becomes that strange dwarf-monster, a white dwarf, fabulously heavy—perhaps of a density that would make a square inch of its material weigh a ton—but emitting very little light-giving radiation. Even if any of the planets of the solar system survived the cataclysm, even if life on any of them could hide itself during this hurricane of super-flame, such life would emerge only into a Universe so cold and black, that death from freezing would take that which had escaped death by incineration.

Chapter XIV

WHERE NOW?

A STRANGE word to write when we are right in the middle of what seems the greatest of Third Acts! And yet what else can one say? We do not know from day to day whether we shall get a word more of news, however enigmatic. We do not know whether the visitors will give us any more; we do not know whether we shall be allowed to receive it. Now that our long smouldering lines of dispute have at one point broken into crackling flame, will not all general news be held up—on the chance that it might give news that ought to be kept under cover.

The reports, however, are still coming in, though Korea may make for general censorship. One report dated 27th June, was still quite clear as far as it went—a high grade, no-doubt-about-it report. Good visibility—over a well-known air route—Las Vegas, Nevada, near the little town of Baker, which is in the desert on the way to the Californian frontier. Good height—14,000 feet. Time, eight minutes past 8 p.m. Good observers (three United Air Lines pilots in their plane, a 'Mainliner'), "Rather like a dirigible," was their description, "cylindrical in shape". The light high up there in that midsummer evening was good enough to enable the colour of this 'tube' type of mystery craft to be seen.

It will be recalled that all the other craft of this type have been seen at night, by their own light or at best with moonlight to help. This one's coloration could be seen—it was bluish with a bright orange tint at the centre. The observers were able to see it well, for it was only some 6,000 feet above them — 20,000 feet up from the ground. It was flying steadily, horizontally and much faster than their own fast plane. They judged in that clear air that it was about twenty miles from them. They were not alone in spotting it. At Las Vegas itself the groundsmen of the Air Port had seen it, and a Navy and an Air Force plane that were up also saw it.

Then on 2nd July another of these big tubes did the tour of the States of Washington and Montana. It swept over 400 miles of route. It was at night, but it looked orange in colour to those who observed it. Air Force and civilian flying officials checked it up. Two Air Port control operators saw it at Spokane, Washington. Another watcher for civilian air companies caught sight of it 160 miles east. At a point 140 miles farther east still, a weather reporter caught sight of it, as did also a Northwest Airlines employee; and, finally, 120 miles on, another reporter saw this 'brilliant object'.

How hard it is to think that 'dirigibles' of this speed and size are a 'secret weapon' of some power on earth.

Then again two young men who live in a suburb of Los Angeles declared that on 25th July, looking up as they drove along in their car at 2.30 a.m. they saw a disc, the dear old-fashioned sort, light in colour, 100 feet in size. It was hovering only about 1,000 feet up, where two big, brightly lit highways intersect. They thought they might track it. But of course it followed traditional manoeuvres—suddenly dashing off. They thought that it left a bluish-white vapour trail.

Are we going to learn any more? Or is the story to end, as we remember some of the long-back stories of such possible visitors did end—end for years—with a few lights waving about, and then emptiness, the sky innocent of any but the troubles we ourselves make for it and in it.

The lights, which may be farewells, have certainly been sighted recently. On 21st June the famous Hamilton Flying Field, which figured — if off-stage — in the first part of this account, was visited. Three airmen saw 'it'. But it was at 1.35 a.m. No planes of earth were over the field then and none landed till dawn. No shape could be made out. But three times in silence at immense speed, "too quick for a jet" said one of the witnesses, a trail which looked like "the flame from a blow-torch" made passes across the area. Was it a light without a carrier? Was it a search-ray doing the rounds, and seeing how things were going at that base? Was it just the end of the tail of an artificial comet, heading back, out of this world, for the quiet of the uppermost sky, for the reasonable, rational peace of Mars?

Perhaps referring to something farthest out of all is a report already given above. But although the machine was very high up and far away, this observation was made by many and in the middle of the day (2nd August, 1.30 p.m.). The show lasted for 20 minutes. It was along the Pacific coast right down to San Francisco; and this 'cloud', seen by hundreds and judged to be some 15,000 feet up, moved against the prevailing wind. It set its course out to sea and gave off hues of green, red, orange and blue. Could it have been the lights of one of the super-space ships waving farewell as they leave us—leave us to what—our doom?

But even these waving lights are now creating their own enigma. If they are farewells they are certainly being done on the grand scale, unlike the modest blinkings that attended the earlier departures.

On 8th August at 3.38 a.m. a green light appeared. It lit up a large area of countryside. The centre of the illumination seems to have been just north of Orange County, the small county that lies south of and next to Los Angeles County. It was seen over four counties, Los Angeles, San Bernardino, San Diego and Riverside —that means that its light covered the greater part of the State of California south of the city of Los Angeles and north as far as Santa Monica Bay. One careful observer noted that it lit up the countryside for some 90 seconds. Down at San Diego it was so bright that an observer at 3.45 a.m. said that the whole sky was alight—like a giant flash bulb of a photographer's camera.

Most people of course tried to consider it a meteor. The green flash was, some said, followed by a white glare. But many air authorities doubted—and with reason—whether it was meteoric. For either the meteor would be travelling obliquely to the surface of the earth and then its immense speed would carry it so fast that the light would quickly die away from where it was first seen: or it would be coming down directly, vertically, when it would strike the earth or at least explode not far above the earth and the noise of even a small meteor exploding is emphatic. But in this instance no sound was reported.

So it remains 'unidentified'—but not unaccompanied. For the next night it was the turn for 'up coast'; and from Salem, Oregon, up to Seattle, Washington, another huge but silent glare lit similarly the night sky. And still they seem to come . . .

The time has arrived to conclude, to summarize what has been said and to ruminate on it. First and foremost, some beings are here. Secondly, these beings are very intelligent and their intelligence seems to be combined—as does not always seem to be the case with ours—with consideration and patience. Perhaps we may even hope, as they are so considerate, that they will not be too patient.

They can be very powerful and yet considerate. The following, one of the very last of the reports, seems to bear out that—that they have high, unknown powers and yet can prevent them causing damage.

On 29th July 1950 at Springfield, Illinois, the Chief Pilot of the Capital Aviation Company of that city was flying his plane. To him up aloft came a blue streak with a reddish flame for tail (four other people below had sighted it). The object coming toward him happened to strike his propellor. There was no sound, the plane did not heave. But terrific light broke out and the "thing" was gone. This was about 11 p.m. No damage of any sort could be found on the plane. This is certainly evidence of a form of power that we do not command. What was the intelligence behind it or where above?

As was said earlier, the conclusions that we reach will of necessity be according to what we think probable. But what has happened to our poor, standard, old-fashioned, common-sense notion of probability? Once 'all sensible men', 'all educated persons' thought much the same about certain basic things. They might vary about detail, but about the great map of things—here is the land of fact and there the ocean of surmise—they had no doubt.

Now the land has been inundated with surmise; and out of the ocean stand up queer stubborn, enigmatic rocks of fact, on which our traffic-steamers of common sense get frightful bumps, and on which some founder. If only we had a clear sensible explanation! But whatever explanation you take, you will have to submit to a painful amount of credulity.

If you say, "It is all hallucination!" hundreds of witnesses as sober, as cautious, and maybe many of them better informed than you, are just dolts, and make fools of themselves for no purpose. What am I to think of my own powers of observation? Are we all going mad and "seeing things"?

Say then "It is a secret weapon"—but do face up to what that involves—do not say it just because it sounds easy. It is not. It means that responsible persons have misled the public. (Remember they never said—"No one anywhere in this world or outside is making flying discs"—they only said, "We are not").

It means also that by letting these vast new inventions stray about on the civilian flying air-lanes, they have endangered the lives of those travelling in planes, risked that these harmless citizen-passengers should be killed, and killed horribly by being burnt to death. No considerate, responsible person, let alone a whole bunch of them, would dream of doing any such thing or taking any such risk. I know it: you know it: we all know it.

And yet... and yet... and yet... The 'Foreign Powers' idea we may cling to, as a man being pushed off a raft into the sea may cling to the smaller spar. We know it is not true. Again they just could not afford, if they had such a grand slam weapon, to throw it away and risk losing the whole bag of secret tricks. That great enigmatic, iron-curtained or iron-masked country—it has plenty of space in which to try out secret weapons if it has them. To send them idly cruising over the United States is not toughness, it not even brag—it is insanity. If they intend war, what a relief to know they have gone off their heads and forgotten the first rules of war-secrecy and surprise!

So we must let go the 'spar' of 'Foreign Powers'. That theory will not hold the weight of argument from which we cannot shake ourselves free, the weight of evidence that cannot be dismissed. Where then can we find rest for our load? To what depth (of space) are we driven to sink?

149

Would to heaven there *were* some easier, nearer and at the same time less hackneyed, less romantic place to rest than Mars! It is so ridiculous, and to use the now dated word, so 'shy-making', to find that we have to take refuge on that H. G. Wells's hide-out, that nest and breeding ground of the least respectable Science Fiction!

Truth cares little for our dignity; hence we so often try to suffocate that *enfant terrible*, that unwanted child of intelligence. It is this impulse, more than dread, which I believe keeps us from considering seriously the Martian hypothesis. There really does not seem much reason to fear that we shall be panicked by a Martian appearing. For what will he be like—as far as we can tell? In all probability a super-bee of perhaps two inches in length. As they have existed for so long on Mars, as it is presumed they now have no enemies—if they ever had—(as we know, Natural Selection is a 'negative force' and clips things back and reduces them to the plainest shapes) then these creatures of a world where intelligence has won total freedom from brutal repressive force— where life is free to be as beautiful as it deserves to be—why then, creatures as sensitive to colour, as gifted with sight as bees, would be as beautiful as the most beautiful of any flower, any beetle, moth or butterfly. A creature with eyes like brilliant cut-diamonds, with a head of sapphire, a thorax of emerald, an abdomen of ruby, wings like opal, legs like topaz—such a body would be worthy of this 'super-mind'. I am sure that toward it our reaction would be:— "what a diadem of living jewels!" It is we who would feel shabby and ashamed, and may be with our clammy, putty-coloured bodies, repulsive!

We must add, in spite of the beauty of insects, in spite of the fact that our somewhat bulging bodies (patchily covered with hair, and for the rest mainly the tint of a toadstool) may not be that acme of aesthetic charm that we have presumed them to be; we must allow that we should find it hard to make friends with anything that had more than two legs and did not stilt about as we do. The place—Mars—is bad enough. The product—insects—makes bad worse. Our intelligence might approve, our aesthetic senses concede, but our 'brute feelings' would shy—as a horse shies at a peacock.

Of course it is all a matter of what our reaction is to what until now has been treated as inconceivable. None of us can be sure of that. "He jests at scars who never felt a wound" says Shakespeare. People who have never been desperately bereaved, write skits about widows. We know what has been the reception given to the statistically established evidence for Extra-sensory Perception by men who considered themselves not only highly educated but scientific, who maintained that they sat down as little children before Fact (the phrase is that of T. H. Huxley).

The truth was (as shown by Huxley himself when, asked to examine some evidence that psychical research was bringing to light, he replied rudely—because, of course, of subconscious fear—that he would not even enquire)—the truth was and is that the elasticity of our minds is not to be stretched indefinitely, simply by the weight of evidence, the force of facts. We have an emotional tolerance as to what we can stand; and when that limit is reached we repress—no student of human nature, no examiner of his own conscience needed Freud to tell him that. So many scientists have never so enquired of themselves, have never examined the instrument—the particular mind-and-emotion complex with which they have to try to grasp the world, by means of which they focus on, and then try to understand 'facts'.

So we come back to the point made when we were discussing earlier the manner in which the evidence has come together, and what we can make of it—what canons we have for establishing the meaning of the observations that have been made. There it was said, everyone in the end must be his own judge. One by one we shall make up our minds. Some may come gradually to the most awkward but best established conclusion. Others may never be able to gain to the freedom that would permit in this extreme respect an open mind. Probably the old will find it harder than the young.

As it is a personal question when we come to this final point, perhaps the final contribution that can be made here is for the reporter to put himself into the report as the last 'exhibit' (as they say in evidence at a trial), the last fragment of evidence. The barrister may put himself in the witness-box: the judge call on himself to testify.

As an average elderly man, the writer of these lines finds himself, when all the data are laid out and arranged, still divided; not "of two minds". The mind has at last been driven to this conclusion . Step by step, for three years, it has been made to retreat to this uncomfortable and indeed scandalous spot. The force of the evidence would not let it halt short of this. It is one's feelings that refuse to follow. Stubbornly they remain earth-bound. They seem to be incurably conventional. Their reaction (which seems immune to evidence) is the old, perpetually disproved cliché:— "It never happened before. It just cannot have happened now." Irrational, but all too natural.

Anyone who is elderly today has seen things happen that all informed, all scientific opinion was, up till that point, certain could not happen.

When Röntgen discovered X-rays he said to his wife, not "How wonderful for the world. How amazed and happy my colleagues will be!" No. Knowing his world and his colleagues as actual persons, he remarked grimly, "Now there'll be the devil to pay!"

Dewar, who made the first vacuum flasks—the Thermos—when his young men began to talk the new physics used to get angry, tell them to stop their fantasy and get back to facts. Haekel, the intense champion of Evolution by Natural Selection, shouted in a conference with the new 'Mendelians', "You are simply throwing back everything, back to Moses!"

Yes, we can see generation after generation, the wise, the authorities, the informed, the specialists, the men who are called by the ambiguous but honourable name, the scientists, telling each believing age that all is now settled, the canon is for all intents and purposes closed. We shall get endless additions to existing evidence for our present laws and experiences, but none that will turn them upside down. And yet, generation after generation, the whole thing moves slowly turning right over. And today we have to own that, though that turning over is going on, we have to take the adjective out of it. We now turn over our fixed opinions. We are forced by facts—as quickly as a boat capsizes. It is wise then to be able to swim and not have to demand a boat of dogmas to carry us.

Yet, though the process has immensely accelerated in our generation, it has been going on for at least 25 centuries—to our certain knowledge. This kind of thing has not been sprung on us. Moreover, we have had plenty of time to notice our reaction to this sort of experience—we go through three phases with a monotonous and rather discouraging regularity. First we say "What rot, what mischievous nonsense! Such a fraud (the reporter of the fact we find detestable) should be shut up. It is as dangerous as it is repulsively ridiculous!" Next we begin to joke about it; the thing, we own, has something of the lewdly funny about it, but of course it is really only a joke with which to tease and upset the pompous. Then, one day, without anyone noticing it, the whole thing has become obvious, banal, boring, a commonplace, only noted to show how hopelessly backward, silly and prejudiced our elders were.

The process is over for the time being. We have adjusted ourselves. But we have learnt nothing, nothing about ourselves. And when the next shock comes, the next break through of unaccepted fact, we react once more in the same way.

The story for Occidental man (the European who has spread till he has reached the Pacific) began in Asia Minor—the Turkey of today—perhaps somewhere about 600 B.C. And each step to let observation and evidence count was fought—and often to the death—because it made men feel they were, at least physically, of less importance than they thought they were.

We certainly have, as an unexamined assumption in all our minds, the innate conviction that we are immensely important, influential, significant, the most advanced creature in the entire Universe. The animals were put in the world for our use though, as a wise vegetarian once said, "I have yet to receive the invoice". The stars were placed in the sky to instruct each of us ahead as to how we may most profitably steer our course and make money. So when the Ionian Philosophers—the first empiricists, fact-finders-and-lovers and free theorists, the first 'scientists', men who wished to experiment, observe, analyse, trace—when these men on the coast of Asia Minor began to speculate, they were soon in trouble.

For their speculations quickly began to question the assumption of man's supreme importance, and his kindred assumption that the world was made and run by beings almost exactly like men ("Men writ large" and "all too human").

When Anaxagoras (born about 500 B.C.) began to suggest that the Sun was not the body of a living God but "a mass of molten metal about the size of the Peleponnese" (the small peninsula in which Greece terminates), he was bitterly attacked, tried for blasphemy (a conviction would have meant death) and acquitted only through the special pleading of his friend Pericles. But he had to fly the city of Athens to which he had gone to live, because it was the centre of Greek culture and open enquiry!

When, after the Greek collapse, free enquiry started again with the Rennaisance, when the Polish Bishop Nicolas Kopernick (Copernicus) began to speculate again about the night sky and how the stars really ran and our earth's relation to them, his friends dared to publish his book only after his death, though it had been circulated in manuscript thirteen years previously. He was cautious even in his actual expressions, and for a short time it seemed that the whole thing might be regarded as a specialists' controversy, a stupid piece of expert dispute and of no concern to sensible men. But soon man's insane suspicion awoke that his self-importance might be in question and there was, in the usual name of theology, the devil to pay.

Giordano Bruno—a rash man who believed that 'facts' could speak and should be spoken of—defied authority in its own lair; and, to the shame of all concerned, to the lasting discredit of their judgment and their charity, was burnt alive.

Galileo's story—which follows historically on Bruno's—is even better known. He, having discovered more facts about the stars and planets, escaped torture and the flame by only recanting. What is not so well known is that Galileo's own mind was anything but free and open to all the evidence. For when he was studying that anomalous planet Saturn, as he had only a small telescope he did not discover the rings—with which he might have been content as they did not disturb his prejudices, his assumptions. What he did see was what everyone using a small telescope does see

154

when he looks at Solar Planet Six. There is a bright body and, on each side of it can usually be seen two less bright bodies —almost like wings on an insect. Then if you watch night after night, one night the wings, the two side bodies, are gone. We now know why. As mentioned above, the disc of the rings is so thin that only a very large modern telescope will show that rim when it is edge-on to the earth.

Galileo did not know this. He could not think what had happened. And while he was in suspense there rushed into his mind the old, superstitious story about the god Saturn. Had he stumbled on evidence that would confirm and not challenge ancient tradition? No more than T. H. Huxley was he "prepared to sit down humbly as a little child before Fact", if fact chose to be disloyal, to change sides and, instead of properly vexing bishops, supported them and vex scientists! Galileo wrote in his diary with indignant wonder, "Does then Saturn indeed" (as the tradition had said) "eat his own children?" Could it be that the hateful, tyrannous, anthropomorphic stick-in-the-muds had after all known more about the stars than he, the great revolutionary pioneer?

The question was too painful. It was impossible. But what if it was true? To ask it was of course to be bound to follow it up— to study and study again, observe and observe. To ask was right enough and, although sufficiently painful, it was less painful than going on to see whether after all the old school had not been wholly wrong. Galileo asked the question; and then his nerve failed. His courage gave out. He did not go on and make the further observations—observations that must in the end, as they did with later enquirers, lead to the wonderful and in its way reassuring discovery of the rings. No, he could not face the risk. We know that he never studied Saturn again.

There are facts too awkward for us to accept, even when we are great pioneer scientists. We fear the results to us personally, to our prestige, and to our prejudices. Earth, however, with man upon it, had been put in its place—Planet Three, and one of the small ones—and—a later addition to our 'demoting'—all of them are the planets of a sun that is only an Orange Dwarf!

But until this generation we clung to two concepts of our

uniqueness, the uniqueness of our station in space and of our place in the whole hierarchy of life. Earth, we said, is the only planet with life, and the solar system the only system with planets. So we are the only life in the Universe—minute but unique, and making up for lack of quantity, for lack of size, by the intensity of our quality, our rarity. Evolution might show that we were sprung from some animal stock; but we alone had reached the top, come out on the platform of intelligence and self-conscious understanding, able to see things steadily and see them whole!

And then at the two ends of our argument we were attacked and both flanks gave way. Hundreds of thousands of suns are now said to have planets. That disposes of our uniqueness. Further, right up against us in the solar system, our companion Mars has life and there is no reason to suppose that it is not in advance of us. While right beside our actual homes—in every bee-hive—there are intelligences—insects that can think, plan, make maps, give bearings, exchange information. They are apparently conscious and they are not even mammals, warm-blooded, big-brained—they are insects. And the life that is on Mars has probably taken to insect form to raise itself to a pinnacle of understanding above our highest reach today.

Our pride is in ruins. But need we feel that life is emptied of significance? Surely, unless we are insane egotists, the opposite is the truth. We have lost our paranoiac loneliness and our dream of utter superiority. But we have found companions, yet, and possible guides minds that have gone ahead of ours. Is not this good news of the highest quality and of the utmost aptness? Shall we reject the possibility out of hand? Are we doing so well on our own? Have we, with our new powers and trust "in man alone", have we done so well? Having conquered all the other species (or at least made them shun us) have we, *Homo* self-styled *Sapiens*, settled down to peace, prosperity and progress? Look at the map, look at the news.

One of our shrewdest observers did indeed remark—even before our present extravagances of uncontrolled violence against one another—"It is doubtful in what form, were they given to such reflections, the 'lower creation', the animals, would conceive of the

Supreme Principle of Good. There can, alas, be no doubt of the
form in which they would imagine the Principle of Evil—as a
white man!" And now a scientific white man means the same
principle of exterminating, pitiless destruction not only for other
species but for our own, for ourselves and for our children.

There seems then, here and now, no right feeling (any more than
right and adequate reason) why we should refuse, with either heart
or mind, the present possibility that hangs over us. It may be an
offer. If so it could not be more apposite. Why should we decline
at least to consider it?